Strays and Relations

STRAYS AND RELATIONS

THE FIVE HOURS AND FOUR DECADES OF DIZZY GREENFIELD

DIZZY GREENFIELD

Many thanks to Gill Harry for the cover illustration.

Matador
9 Priory Business Park,
Wistow Road, Kibworth Beauchamp,
Leicestershire. LE8 0RX
Tel: 0116 279 2299
Email: books@troubador.co.uk
Web: www.troubador.co.uk/matador
Twitter: @matadorbooks

Published by Matador in association with Silver Crow Books
www.silvercrowbooks.co.uk

ISBN 978 1788039 345

British Library Cataloguing in Publication Data.
A catalogue record for this book is available from the British Library.
Printed on FSC accredited paper
Printed and bound in Great Britain by 4edge Limited

Typeset in 11pt Minion Pro by Troubador Publishing Ltd, Leicester, UK

Matador is an imprint of Troubador Publishing Ltd

To my brother because I love you,
and of course, for all the strays.

On July 21st 1968, eighteen-year-old Marie Kennedy went into premature labour. At the time, she didn't realise she was carrying twins. The labour took forty-eight hours.

The babies – both girls – weighed less than four pounds each. They were taken to the special care unit of the hospital. The nursing staff did not expect the more poorly of the twins to survive; they called the Catholic priest to baptise both the infants.

As feared, only one twin lived. Marie Kennedy, the mother, hoped to take her remaining daughter home. In the end, though, she left hospital alone. This is the story of what happened thirty-six years later…

CHAPTER 1

On The Train

I sat alone on the train, having declined all offers from the many kind friends who had volunteered to join me. They understood that this was something I had to face on my own. All the same, after five hours with no-one to distract my thoughts, I was becoming ever more anxious; I put on more lipstick, brushed my hair, checked my phone yet again. I was sure the guard had been eyeing me suspiciously since Birmingham, but my days of ticket avoidance were long gone. Finally, I put the brush and phone away. I had nothing left to do now but stare out of the window.

In stark contrast with our soft West-Country fields, the view from the train was one of grey industrial warehouses and factories, mostly derelict-looking, all of which added to the general feeling of depression in this area. *Who would want to live here?*

A large woman and her small son entered the aisle; I hadn't noticed them boarding the train, but she filled the narrow gangway. Edging closer with the toddler and assorted bags of paraphernalia, she plonked herself down in the seat opposite me. On my half of the table there was a notebook, pen, and takeaway coffee. But her half was soon overflowing into mine with wet wipes, discarded toys, and half-eaten sandwiches, invading *my* space. The toddler upturned his mother's bag, throwing crayons, empty crisp packets and nappies onto the floor, obviously intent on finding the sweets that his mother kept telling him he wasn't allowed to eat until he had finished his lunch.

'I told you to eat that sandwich, Scot. I'm goin' to effin' kill yer if you don't behave.' Her broad accent, a dialect unfamiliar to my ears, sounded harsh.

Scot clamped his mouth shut as she tried to force the doughy white bread between his lips. Pale and scruffy, he looked like a decent meal and some warm clothes wouldn't go amiss. His head was shaven and two green snot bubbles dripped from sore-looking nostrils. He pushed his mother and her sandwich away with his closed fist then looked up at me. I winked at him and he grinned, but his red eyes showed he had cried already today.

'The little sod's been really hard work since he got up this mornin',' the mother said, addressing me.

'Perhaps he needs a nap,' I suggested.

'What he needs is a wee, but he won't go.' Then, through clenched teeth, 'DO YOU WANT A WEE, SCOT?'

The toddler shook his head, bringing an expression of rage to his mother's face. Her jaw twisted, contorted. 'If you wet yourself on this train, and I mean it this time, I'm goin' to smack you.'

How kind of her, I thought, *to have shared the intimate details of Scot's urinary efforts with the rest of the carriage.* But I smiled at her, attempting what I thought was a sympathetic expression, hoping that would make her less angry with Scot, then stared at my cup of coffee.

She leaned back in her seat, crossed her arms over her ample chest, and gave me the once over. I expect she thought that it was all right for the likes of me, no toddler to deal with or to potty train, out on a jolly. After a few more minutes, they started up again, but this time she lost patience with Scot. She dragged him from his seat by his arm. *Should I call social services now?* The yells got fainter as the toddler was manhandled down the carriage to the toilet.

This spectacle had upset me so much that my own eyes were prickling with tears; seeing Scot's distress was the last straw for me. I hated seeing children unhappy; hated seeing parents making children unhappy. My mum, Paula, put it down to me being overly sensitive; for a moment I was gripped by panic. *I need to get off this train!*

Instead of pulling the communication cord, I took a deep breath and sipped my coffee. Then I rummaged in my bag for my mobile, to see if my friend, Sugar, had texted me again.

Sugar was one of my dearest friends, and godmother to my daughter. We had met when we were both working at a wildlife park. She'd been my lifeline on that journey – keeping up a steady text support service all day, even though she was *meant* to be concentrating on giving a work presentation in the Canary Islands. There was another message now:

'They are going to love you, Dizzy, everything will be grand. True, Brave and Fearless remember?'

'Thanks, Sugar,' I replied, *'but right now I wish I could go home.'*

Scot and his mother were heading back down the carriage towards me. Scot's face was red and blotchy, his mother's face determined, satisfied. I guessed that she had got her way and managed to enforce her offspring's compliance. It was then I noticed her pregnancy bump. How would she cope? I wondered how I would have turned out if I'd been brought up by another mother than Paula, in a regime of imposed urination.

The journey seemed interminable – but now it was ending. I wanted it to end – and didn't want it to end. Was terrified of the meeting ahead.

The train slowed down as it approached the platform and I made my way to the exit with growing dread.

As I stood by the doors waiting to disembark, I found I wasn't alone. Beside me was a man with his head in his jacket, sniffing glue. He came up for air, raising his head out of his jacket just enough to squint at the light, while still masking his joy under his coat.

'What are you doing here?' he asked me.

'Just visiting,' I told him. 'I haven't been here before.'

'The best way to see this city is from a distance, love. I'd just keep going if I were you. It's a fuckin' awful place.'

He tucked his head back inside his coat, then turned away but his words made me think... He was far from being a reliable travel advisor, but the idea of going back home was getting more attractive. Had I made the right decision to come?

There was still time to disappear; it wouldn't matter – *it wouldn't be personal if I hadn't actually met her, would it?* I could stay on-board, jump off at the next station and catch a connection home.

As the train ground to a halt alongside the platform, my stomach lurched. My journey was at an end – a journey that had taken five hours and four decades.

CHAPTER 2

WILL OF IRON

It was my partner, Will's fault I was even on the train – and my fault, of course, for falling in love with him in the first place.

If that hadn't happened; if I hadn't moved away from my adoptive family to live with him all those years ago; if Will hadn't encouraged me to go searching for my birth mother – if Will hadn't been so bloody supportive, I probably wouldn't be on this stupid train.

He kept saying it would be good for me.

'I think you need to know where you're from, Diz. Your mum thinks so too. You keep dashing from one thing to the next; it's like something's missing in you that you're trying to fill. Your mum and I just want you to be happy!' Then he'd grin. Will was like that, always grounded, always wanting the best for everyone – sometimes his unfailing good nature was hard to cope with!

We hadn't had the easiest of starts together. With only a selection of donated furniture and family cast offs, we had moved into the rickety farmhouse that had been occupied by Will's family since the 1940s. We were excited about the future.

In truth though, it was only love that kept the quirky house from falling down. As the colours deepened in the woods that surrounded us, Mother Nature threatened to get hold of our dreams, tried to blow them away in a gust of autumnal disappointment. We were putting out new shoots, tentatively wrapping them round the ancestral roots put down by Will's family in the decades before us, entwining with them so we too could become rock-steady. The cold reality of a draughty house with no heating, plus long hours on the farm for Will, was bad enough. If he hadn't been so very placid, we wouldn't have lasted until the spring, let alone for the last seventeen years. But the main problem, even after all our spats over the years, was that during that first winter I missed my mum, Paula. And then there were the fixtures and fittings! Amid the emulsion paint, young love and renovations, we started the battle with the resident Rayburn. Most people would have thrown it out and bought a cooker, but the Rayburn was vital. We had both grown up with one. A Rayburn had kept warm the kitchens of both our respective childhoods.

But neither of us had lived with such a badly-behaved stove, one that had such spirit. The Rayburn, whom we loved and called Daphne, hated us in return, but, as she was our only source of heat and cooking, we battled on, trying to tame her. She billowed smoke from her crevices even on the stillest days when there wasn't even a light breeze to upset her temperamental flue. Daphne continued to have a laugh at our expense at every given opportunity. Often, her ovens struggled to become lukewarm – any request seemed a bit too much of an effort for her. A roast dinner could take her anywhere from between six to eight hours. Other days, her oven raged at temperatures more suited to a crematorium.

My mother, Paula, became increasingly worried about Christmas dinner.

'Would you like to come over here, my love?'

'No, thank you, it's our first Christmas in our very own

home. Come here to us. Wouldn't you like a country Christmas, Mum?'

'Um, well, yes… it's just you're not used to that Rayburn, are you? You've only ever used a microwave. Would you like the one we have here at home by the way?'

'No. thank you. I don't believe in microwaves now. I'm going to cook everything in Daphne. It will be magical. Leave it to me.'

Will acquired a turkey from one of his farming mates, and I made promising preparations with sage stuffing, a phone call to my Mum, and the help of an onion.

'Daphne's trying to die,' said Will. He knelt down and opened the bottom door to shove more coal and logs into her cavernous depths, trying to coax her into life. 'There's nothing for it,' he continued. 'I'll have to get the blowtorch.'

'My mum, Al and your mother will be here in less than three hours and you can't blowtorch a turkey' I said, 'It has to go in the oven.'

'It's nothing I can't handle,' said Will, heading out to his workshop.

He returned a few minutes later with blowtorch in hand.

'Stand back, Diz, this'll teach Daphne a lesson.' Will reached into his overalls pocket for a Zippo lighter. He lit the gas. Bending over he held out the blowtorch at arm's length, turned his head away, and shoved his hand into the dark, unknown void that held the mysterious workings of Daphne.

But she was spiteful. Not only that, she was older and wiser. She must have been getting on for sixty years of age and she obviously thought she should retire. Clearly, she had made mincemeat of better cooks than me over the years and wasn't given to helping a novice girl attempt her first Christmas lunch. Incensed by the use of the blowtorch, Daphne flew into a fiery rage. One minute the turkey was still so raw it was quivering then, moments later, it had shrunk closer to the size of a sparrow and its once pink flesh turned crow black.

Will lifted up the tin foil that hid his superb free-range bird, then stumbled backwards as the smell of the charcoaled remains hit him. Our two greyhounds, who had been waiting patiently at his feet for a little pre-lunch morsel, turned in disgust and wandered back to their beds.

The lunch was late. We finally ate what was left of Daphne's and my combined effort at four o'clock in the afternoon.

'Well, Dizzy, that was a very good Christmas lunch, considering the problems with the oven,' Mum said, setting down her knife and fork. She always said something positive, years of being a teacher had trained her well, but the look on her face gave her away. She smiled across the table debris at Will.

Will's mum fought with the blackened turkey, stoic in her efforts to keep going. Her cutlery scraped across the plate and her knife clinked against the bird's bones as she battled with the scorched sinews of the overdone offering. She was polite right up to the bitter end of the carcass.

'Still, it's thanks to you we had a lunch, Will. You always sort everything out,' said Mum.

Sometimes, I thought my mum preferred Will to me, but who could blame her?

We left the table and moved into the front room, where Will set another small blaze into life and he and I settled back onto the sofa. The greyhounds slumbered away the winter's day on their beanbag, curled back on themselves as long dogs do, resting their heads on each others' backs.

During the coffee and mints, there was small talk about our plans for the renovation of the farmhouse and when we'd be taking delivery of the ewes we had ordered. I even had a quick tidy round, piling red and gold wrapping paper onto Will's fire. But achieving a successful Christmas was still "mission unaccomplished."

It was while Will and I were washing up in the kitchen, that we smelt the acrid whiffs quite unlike the normal woody smell that I found comforting in the winter. Then a few black plumes billowed back down the chimney into the front room.

By the time anyone registered alarm, the smoke had begun spreading throughout the rest of the house, curling up the stairs in a lethargic but menacing way, as if pretending not to mean it. We had another flue emergency on our hands. There was, as Will put it, 'Something wrong with the asshole of a chimney.'

*

'Fire's out now, Diz,' said Will, sometime later. His face was so carbon-blackened, only the whites of his eyes were showing. He began shovelling tar and soot from the fireplace into a muck-encrusted wheelbarrow that he had brought across the new carpet into the front room.

'Wasn't exactly the Christmas we planned, was it?' I said.

'Well, it's one that'll leave a lasting a memory, that's for sure,' he replied.

Eventually, though, when the house was quiet, when the floorboards had creaked and groaned a last protest, I sighed with relief and scrambled into bed and lay snuggled up between Will and the hounds. I thought about my nan and wished that she could be still alive, to have spent one more Christmas with us. I thought about all the missing people whom we loved.

The last thing I did that Christmas night was to think about my birth mother, Marie. I thought about her every birthday and every Christmas. Now that I was settled, despite Daphne and the mayhem, I had started to get the feeling that I would like to know more about her.

The law had recently changed. According to Jenny Murray and *Woman's Hour*, adopted children who had reached eighteen were now able to put their names onto a contact register. They were also able to have access to their birth file. That first Christmas night I decided: when the lambing was over in the late spring, I would investigate the contact register further. I tried to think about my plans, but sleep danced tantalisingly before me until I could no longer resist her charms.

Even so, without Will and the non-stop support, I might not have gone to see the social worker… let alone been on this ruddy train.

CHAPTER 3

FIFTY SHADES OF BEIGE

Beige, I decided, is the default colour option for elderly people, school semolina, and rooms where you meet social workers.

'Dervla?'

Lyn, the social worker, handed me a blue cardboard covered file. Since 1968, its thin frame had been held precariously together with treasury tags. The two pieces of green string with metal ends bound the secrets of the past. I will always remember the excitement of being on the edge of finding out. Finding out my birth parents' full names, addresses of where they had lived, the reasons why they had given me away. Perhaps, hidden inside the folder would be the answer as to why I wasn't good enough. I will also never forget the feeling of thirty years of not knowing.

'Take your time.'

Lyn sat with her hands on her knees. She was wearing neatly pressed white linen trousers and a black tunic top. I was glad she wasn't doing "the face" that I'd seen some welfare types adopt, pretending to care. This one was far too professional. Her poker straight dark hair was parted, unimaginatively, in the middle, making curtains around her long pale face. Her eyes gave nothing away. It must be very difficult to know where to look in these situations.

She reached forward and sifted quietly through her handbag that lay between us on the small grey table. I stared at the wall above her head; looking at a picture. I knew it was a print of a Constable because of the wooden wagon in the river, the little liver-and-white spaniel on the bank, and because my nan used to have the same print on her sitting-room wall. It was a picture from my childhood, when all was warm and secure. It was familiar, but in the wrong place.

The silence was uncomfortable; it was reminiscent of sitting in the school headmistress's office, waiting for bad marks, and I'd certainly had my fair share of those. I stared at the file, then carefully opened it and flicked through the aged sheaves of paper like I was looking for a guilty secret. Some of the sheets were photocopied. It felt as though I wasn't important enough to have the originals, even though this was my story.

Among the typed A4 sheets were a few handwritten letters, slipped in between like an afterthought. Worn thin, like tracing paper, with scribbled notes in the margins, now faded. It was all a bit of a mess. I rummaged amongst the papers, not knowing where to begin. Eventually, I caught sight of a copy of the letter that was sent to my adoptive parents in 1969.

Dear Mr and Mrs Greenfield,

Now that the adoption order has been made, I am sure that you would like to have some written details about your adopted daughter;

One of twin girls, her birth weight was 4lbs. Her twin sister died shortly after birth.

Because of her low birth weight your baby spent some weeks in the special care unit at the hospital where she was born.

Her Mother is aged 18. Auburn hair, green eyes, 5'5" tall, attractive. She has a pleasant friendly manner.

The baby's Father, aged 22, is a signalman in Her Majesty's Forces. He attended secondary modern school and went into the army at the age of 15 on a long term 12-year engagement. He enjoys sport, including skiing, dancing and football.

And that's all my adoptive parents were sent. They hadn't been allowed to view the file that lay in my hands now. Nobody had seen this letter since 1969. I thought how poorly informed they had been, how I got more information than this when I rescued a dog from the RSPCA.

Every piece of information about my birth father was on British Army headed paper. There were many other forms in the file, although my twin's medical history had been shielded from view. Someone had thought to place a blank sheet over her before they photocopied the form that we shared.

The documents reeked of a time when the state, and in this case the Roman Catholic Church, bullied people into decisions, "for their own good". The forms betrayed this. The other information about my parents came from the following notes from the social worker who dealt with my adoption at the time:

Mother. Estimated level of intelligence:
Average.
An assessment of the mother's personality, temperament and maturity. Her motivation for adoption and attitude towards the baby. Is she articulate and readily available to discuss her difficulties?
I had a long interview with the mother. Attractive, vivacious girl. She has quite a strong character but is not very intelligent.
At this interview the natural mother (now Mrs Kennedy),

actually brought the baby with her! She had taken her for a walk from the foster mother's. There were a lot of interruptions while she tried to deal with the baby who was upset, missing her carer.

Father. Estimated level of intelligence: The social worker hadn't even bothered to write anything for my father, but she had noted down that apparently my paternal grandmother was married to a nurse who was employed, in a *mental hospital* (her language).
Well, I thought, that could come in handy.

Physical appearance of baby:
Very attractive looking, pretty, small features, turned up nose. Nicely proportioned. Foster carer says baby sleeps well at night but has a pronounced temper!!
Mrs Kennedy has vacillated and is still perhaps rather confused.
Father... free from any disease (VD).

Neither my adoptive or birth parents would have been privy to this information, which until this moment had been a heavily-protected secret. The patronising tone of the sixties-social worker and the awful attitude towards my birth mother at the time of the adoption made its impact. Baby girls were at a premium on the adoption circuit in the 1960s.

I absorbed the longed-for pages, including a brown envelope with *confidential* stamped across the top left-hand corner. The envelope was addressed to Mrs Kennedy but, on closer inspection, it was empty. This letter had clearly been back and forth through the postal system. As well as bearing three different addresses, there was a typed message on the front, written in purple.

Gone Away 255.

Lyn interrupted me. I sensed that my allotted time was up.

'You could put your name forward on the contact register. If any members of your family are already on it you will be contacted.'

'I'm not sure how to do that,' I said.

She carried on, regardless. 'Or you could do a search at the library… there are organisations that could help you. The Salvation Army or NORCAP for instance.'

For now, holding the birth file was enough. I stood up to make my move.

'Don't hesitate to get in touch with me if you need any support,' she said.

I thought, *I might need support if what Lyn had told me came true.* During the compulsory hour-long counselling session, she had been careful to point out the pitfalls.

'There are cases where the mother became pregnant as a result of rape,' she explained. 'You may not have thought about these things. Adoptions do occur because of abuse in families, or neglect. I'm not saying that's the case here, but until you find out more these are things you need to bear in mind.'

One size must fit all. *How can these people reel off their scripts, making them sound genuine?* But Lyn hadn't finished with me yet.

'Be careful, proceed with grace. Even if you do find family members, remember they may be remarried. They may have new partners and children who know nothing about their past.'

In other words, my "family" may not want to meet me. I just couldn't tolerate another rejection. It was too much of a risk.

On my way out, I thanked the sagging receptionist ensconced in her sterile booth. She didn't lift her head. It looked like abuse from dysfunctional families had taken its toll on her. What an unforgiving place that social work building was, its foundation built from family disaster, its walls shielding the secrets of people's lives, its locked clandestine cabinets hiding away all that information. *This is what happens when the state takes control. I thought; emotion can't be permitted to creep through.*

I clasped the birth file to my chest. The receptionist finally looked up as I struggled with one hand to open the heavy front door. Old and huge, it was cloaked in thick black layers. Paint flaked from its hinges, jarring under my nails as I turned the handle.

'Can you manage?' she asked.

I squeezed myself through a tiny gap, wedging the door open with my foot.

'I can,' I replied.

The door thudded shut behind me, protecting other people's secrets, keeping them safe.

Glad to be back out in the spring sunshine, I hurried to my mum's house, clasping my roots now held in a white carrier bag. Back out into the real world again, after the shock of it all. I wasn't prepared. The bubble hadn't burst.

A car horn blasted. I was standing at the start of the zebra crossing, not watching, not even paying attention to the cars that had stopped to let me cross. The sound of that horn made me cry; that one action was my final awakening.

'Silly cow! Think I've got all day?' the driver yelled. Wheels spinning, he drove off, pushing his fist out of the window, sticking up his middle finger. I walked quickly, then ran a few steps. I couldn't cope with this on my own. Mum would make sense of it all.

Home smelled of porridge oats, warm milk and safety. My mother, although once a home-economics teacher, had in later years become a big fan of the microwave. The milk was heated to within an inch of its life, scalding the porridge oats into a rude morning awakening. Porridge was accompanied by breakfast TV with Wincey Willis and the Green Goddess.

Unfortunately, since the decorator had been in, my always-in-residence beige mother had become doubly difficult to spot.

Today, she was almost completely camouflaged from view. Her new ecru sofa and matching walls, along with her off-white cardigan and trousers meant it was hard to make her out. My mother was only visible because of her blue socks. She sat on her new sofa, legs dangling over the edge – her feet didn't reach the floor – like a little girl. Even her shoes were taupe.

I expected mum to be in her normal place in the kitchen, instead of languishing in her light-tan interior. So, I was at a disadvantage from the start. I stomped in, slamming the birth file down onto the kitchen table for maximum effect, hating its contents.

'Here it is, my bloody birth file. It's all here, have a look if you want.'

It was all a bit embarrassing as I was talking to myself. And, of course, I wanted her to fall upon it immediately, intrigued as I was about every detail – once I'd retrieved her from the sofa, she didn't disappoint me.

First, though, Mum made tea. She stood next to the kettle waiting. It took an age, like it does when you boil it in the middle of the night, or when you've had bad news. Whilst the kettle boiled, she eyed me warily, watching for hints of an imminent meltdown. But she did seem excited that at least we finally had some information. We sat side by side at our comforting kitchen table and peered into the blue folder, which was already precious to me. We came across a letter from my birth mother giving permission for me to be adopted. At last, we could see her first name.

'I was right about your mother's name being Marie then? That's all we knew,' said Mum.

'She's not my mother.' I spat the words out.

'Well, you know what I mean.'

'You're my mother.'

She carried on. 'And your father was in the Forces. Well, we were told that… oh, but I didn't know your mother had been so young'. She hung her head slightly, biting her bottom lip.

'This isn't about me needing anyone else to be my mum, it's

just I need to know why it happened. To know what they're like. I love you. You're my mum,' I told her.

She put her arm around my shoulders and I felt the tears trying to sting through. I wouldn't let them, though. I swallowed, pushing back my emotions, and lay my head on her shoulder.

'Gosh, it must be difficult for you to see this, love,' she said, rubbing my arm.

We sipped tea. Its syrupy liquid warmed us, seeping through the stark, new reality until it brought us back to a place of familiarity.

We spent one hour… three hours… who knows?… going through the file, piecing together the fragmented life of Marie. The horror of her situation hit us both.

*

It wasn't that I wanted to meet my birth mother – not then. I just wanted to know who she was and that she was okay – that she'd survived. I'd wanted this ever since I'd been a child and first found out about being adopted, back in the times of my mother and The Great Craft Movement.

CHAPTER 4

THE GREAT CRAFT MOVEMENT

My first memory wasn't being told I was adopted. There were many other memories before that day. Besides, the subject was never given much attention, barely interrupting The Great Craft Movement (GCM) that was going on in our house at the time – it was this that made up my earliest memories and absorbed us all throughout my childhood.

During that period in our family's history, my mum was centre stage, mid way through one of her obsessions and gripped by the artistic muse. It would have been fine if we had lived up a Welsh mountain, or on Bodmin Moor. A bleak location would have suited all our personalities, and somewhere spacious would have been more apt, but no, we had a modern bungalow in a narrow-minded street, where our neighbours didn't go in for creativity in the main.

Mum's crafts spanned many mediums. First, there was the pottery phase. A kiln was installed in the garage. Mum would tie a red-and-white spotted headscarf over her curls, don some brown corduroy flares and disappear for hours. She would re-appear with pottery dragons, unusually-shaped pots and generally-unidentifiable clay objects, all lovingly constructed in the name of art.

She had been an art student, so it wasn't a surprise that she enjoyed herself in the garage. But over time, unchecked, the GCM took over our lives. It flounced in under the front door one day when we weren't paying attention and, before long, started to seriously encroach on our living space.

The pottery phase hadn't been too bad; the dragon that mum produced was her favourite. My brother, Ellis, and Dad, Terry, probably weren't that bothered about it, but Nan dusted him weekly, giving him the once over with her feather duster.

Nan unimaginatively called him Puff. He had pride of place next to the electric bar fire in our "lounge". This room had been carefully decorated in orange and brown, with black undertones. It was completed by our mum's pride and joy, a cream shag-pile carpet – which Ellis and I took turns to rake on a Saturday morning.

Other lesser mortals on our street only had a "front room". We obviously thought we were a cut above, as reflected in our home furnishings. According to Ellis we were the first family to have continental quilts, not eiderdowns and blankets, the high-maintenance shag-pile, and a Moulinex electric cheese grater (also in a shameless shade of orange).

Ellis was especially pleased to receive his continental quilt, because he could ditch the bri-nylon bed covers. For years he had been manufacturing an electrical spark by rubbing his legs together very quickly under the top bed sheet. By wearing pyjamas that were also from the same unforgiving Brentford bri-nylon material and turning all the lights off, he managed to carry out his very own electrical experiment at No. 12, St. Normal Street, Midsummer Boring.

Our high street was the most tedious one in the world; we didn't even have a Woolworths. Even so, when Mum met her teacher friends as she walked through town, she liked to use her "Posh Voice", the same dulcet tones as when she met Mrs Pomfrit, the vicar's wife, or when she answered the telephone. Ellis said she'd obviously been practising.

The second phase of the GCM was weaving. The table-top loom was a real pain in the arse as it had to sit on the dining room table; it resided there for months. My brother and I still managed to eat our tea, but every time we viewed each other it was through lines of thread, making our faces look slightly distorted. Still, we pressed on with our fish and chips, pausing only to remove the odd dollop of splattered ketchup from the latest garment being created. Ellis and I grumbled until finally the loom went back out to the garage.

Mum was meant to be making a rug, but really, she preferred macramé to the loom. She produced plant holders that collapsed and owls with shiny brown beads for eyes. And so, after months of effort with the rug making, she emerged triumphant from the garage only having managed to produce four small brown woven table mats. We all gathered round as Mum put the mats on the table and stared silently at the pathetic result of her months of hard labour.

Ellis was the first to speak. 'Very good Mum, but there are five of us.'

Dad smiled to himself, winked at Ellis, and went immediately back to his chair, where he spent the rest of the day quietly humming and playing his guitar. Nan, mouth set in tight disappointment, reached for a crinkled hanky from the pocket of her house coat and blew her nose.

'Must get back to my pastry,' she said.

She turned on her slippered heels and shuffled back to the kitchen.

Phase three brought an easel and a selection of oil paints. These could be transported, so sadly they decided to come on holiday with us to Scotland. Unfortunately for me, my sixteen-year-old brother, who was trying desperately hard to leave home, had more sense than to accompany us. So, with no brother to annoy, one parent off fly-fishing and one painting happily away by the river bank, my six-year-old self and I had the dullest holiday that side of Gretna.

Phase four was gardening. Let's just say that, even now, as proper grown-up adults, if Ellis and I must visit a garden centre we need to be given medication.

Amid the GCM, somewhere between the kiln and the loom, the paintings and the plants, my past got lost.

Finding out about my adoption didn't happen until I was six years old, just after that holiday – there had been no earlier revelation. Such a life-changing event should surely have been the defining moment in my childhood, but we were too busy being a family. The subject wasn't treated as trivial, but there were no dramatic scenes or hysteria.

One evening, my parents, Ellis, Nan and our springer spaniel all came into the bathroom. They perched on the toilet lid, on the bathmat, and ever so casually, at the back bit of the bath where the leftover brown tiles had been used to make a shelf.

My dad crossed one leg over the other in a casual 1970's magazine pose. He balanced a glass of whisky on his knee, Dave Allen-style, swilling the Bells around the glass so that the smooth mahogany liquid caressed the sides. He held the glass gently and, with the other hand, smoked a Players No.6. He had even brought his ash tray in with him.

They all peered over the edge of the bath at me. I knew that something was going to be announced, because the dog never peered unless it was serious, so I fretted with the hot tap and allowed more warmth to run into the bath by way of a distraction.

I pretended to understand the news they delivered – something about there being a lovely Irish lady called Marie who was my 'real' mum. Marie hadn't been able to keep me, so she had given me to them to take care of. It all sounded delightfully simple.

Marie was very sad to have had to do this, they said, and it wasn't my fault. It wasn't that she didn't love me. In fact, she loved me so much that she had found a home for me where I would be taken care of and loved. They explained that she hadn't wanted her baby to go away.

'It was the saddest thing in the world for her,' Mum said. 'But we are ever so pleased to have you and to be your mummy and daddy.'

'We didn't have to have you,' Dad said, 'we chose you.' He grinned at me and had a swig of his whisky.

'Where did you get me from?' I asked.

'From the foster carer,' he said. 'But you're ours now, we love you.'

'And what would our life be like without you?' Mum carried on. 'Your being adopted doesn't mean we love you less.'

I was loved as much as my brother Ellis but, from then on, I knew I was a fake. My brother on the other hand, was the real thing.

I patted bubbles onto my pale, freckly knees and squeezed the foam through my fingers wishing their truth was a lie. Sodden plaits made my auburn hair appear darker; they hung uncomfortably across my wet shoulders. I couldn't look my parents in the eye – brown unlike my own green ones.

'Can I call you Paula and Terry then please, not Mummy and Daddy?'

They gulped and smiled. The birthday card they gave me a few weeks later had that same uneasy sentiment.

It read, "Happy Birthday darling, all our love always, Paula and Terry (Mummy and Daddy)" followed by the predicted xxx.

But, although I had lost my own Marie, my birth mother, someone, somewhere must have been trying to make it up to me. Now I was a very real part of the family that adopted me, not only one Mum, Paula, but two – the second in the disguise of Nan, to fuss over me. I was blessed with "Mother Overload".

I had fallen on my feet, and landed, somehow, in a terrific home. I didn't know how lucky I was to have ended up with such a family. I had the luck of the Irish. "We aren't your actual birth parents", was a saying that was sometimes repeated over the years. Other than these odd occasions, though, the subject was never given much attention – it was something I just accepted. But my ears always pricked up when I heard the phrase 'up for adoption' spoken by adults around me or on the TV. It made adoption sound like the adoptees had chosen their situation and were up for a bit of an adventure. But which adopted family you ended up with seemed to me to be a bit like the game of Monopoly that we played at Christmas. A game where you can land on the wrong number in an instant, but change your future chances forever.

You could "Go to jail", with no "Get out of jail free card". Or you could end up with "Water Works" when you were secretly praying for "Mayfair".

We all got on with our lives – Ellis got married to Mags and moved down the road. And then my dad, Terry, came home in the middle of the night and said that he was leaving.

The Great Craft Movement ended abruptly; it took my mother years to paint another picture.

CHAPTER 5

IRELAND

It wasn't all Will's fault though – what happened next was my best friend, Sugar's responsibility.

We had become friends at the Wildlife Park, where we both spent our days pretending to be working; in the main, though, it was acting the fool that we managed best, rather than any actual productive activity. The silliness cemented our friendship.

Although we saw each other daily, it was normal for Sugar and me to phone each other every time there was something wrong in our lives. I made an emergency call to her. Our phone conversation consisted of two lines. It went something like this.

'I've got the birth file,' I said.

'I'm bringing wine. Be with you in an hour,' she replied.

Real friends know exactly what to do. It had taken me years to pluck up the courage to access my adoption records. Sugar had been keeping watch; she knew how important this was.

So, late that evening, long after Will had gone to sleep, Sugar arrived. It took her twenty-nine minutes, even though it was, on average, a forty-five-minute drive from her house to ours. The dogs heard her first, drawn from their slumbers even before her car screeched to a standstill. Her wheels scattering the gravel on the driveway drove them into a frenzy. But after this dramatic arrival, Sugar's tap on the front door was gentle – as if she really was trying not to disturb anyone.

The figure I let in was wearing a black beanie hat, clasping a bottle of Sauvignon Blanc and looking worried. The dogs crowded round, relieved that this wasn't a burglar, but a familiar friend. She greeted them through the wagging tails and canine kisses. We tiptoed through the house to the kitchen and I got out two glasses while Sugar stood by the Rayburn watching me, cautious, assessing the situation.

'Oh, Dizzy...' she said, finally.

'It's all right, missus. You know, it's all right.' Sugar and I had a habit of calling each other missus – it has been a bit of a joke at first and now it was a mark of our friendship.

Throughout that night, we scanned the birth file for hidden clues. We lay the family secrets bare. But, even after several hours of searching, we were still unable to find any definite information about Marie's Irish family, or where they had lived. It became obvious that the search was fruitless. The tentative link with Killarney was from information that had been given to my adoptive parents by the social worker nearly thirty years ago. Sugar finally closed the file and made an announcement.

'Well, there's nothing for it, we'll have to go to Ireland and find them ourselves. Let's book the ferry now.'

So a month later we boarded the Fishguard to Rosslare night ferry. We set sail, unaware that the adventure ahead was to be the bumpiest two weeks of my life so far.

It was all calm to begin with on the crossing, but with several hours to spare before bedtime, we took up our normal default position for any tricky situation; in other words, we went to the bar. Our imaginations full of promise and intrigue, we finished our second bottle of dry boat-white before heading back down to the cabins.

Unable to grasp whether it was the boat or Sugar lurching from side to side, I clutched the narrow corridor walls and followed her along dimly-lit passageways in search of our accommodation. After half an hour of being unable to find the cabin, she brought us back up the stairs, out into the safety of the bar. We had another drink.

We were somewhat surprised to eventually find the cabin, whereupon I fell through the door into the small toilet cubicle. The toilet was positioned directly in line with the bathroom door. I adopted the sitting position just as a huge wave passed under the boat. The door was flung open, revealing me peeing for Ireland.

Sugar went into a kind of frenzy. She laughed for three hours, and so we ended up only having twenty-two minutes of sleep before the ferry docked.

In Rosslare, we found a single café that was open. Here, to our relief, we were presented with huge mugs of dark liquid by a rather little woman. Unfortunately, the tea bags were still floating in the brew. It was barely seven o'clock in the morning and I could hardly open my eyelids.

'Get this down you now, girls,' twittered our waitress in a strong Irish accent. She crashed the plates down in front of us. We nicknamed her Mrs Birdlike, because of how she chirped her way around the café.

I prodded at the breakfast. The black-and-white pudding clung to the sides of the dish as though fighting for its life. Somewhere underneath lurked the bacon, next to the soggy hash browns. Everything was drowning in a sea of lard.

Mrs Birdlike watched us battle to eat, her beady eyes making sure we didn't attempt to leave anything. With the breakfasts served, her work was over. She could now set about her true calling in life, to find out gossip about holiday makers. She was determined in her task. Her method, it seemed, was to ask one hundred searching questions of us. She was expert. She should have joined the police service, cooking up information instead of cooking up breakfasts. After only a few carefully-planned, but leading initial questions she effortlessly secured sufficient information about us to begin her interrogation. Before we knew it, we had confessed the area where we lived. Mrs Birdlike was off.

'Do you know my cousin, Kitty O'Brien? She lives in the West Country, near Bristol,' she chirped.

We imagined she thought the West Country very small indeed, as if there was probably only the one village. Sugar pretended to rack her brain. Her actions became more animated as she scratched her head, bit her bottom lip and looked ever so interested. Her concern had her asking Mrs B for a full description of Kitty. Sugar surprised all three of us.

'I think I probably have met your Kitty. It was on a night out for St Patrick's.' Sugar hesitated. 'But of course, I can't be sure.'

I glared at her as she finished off her baked beans.

'What did she look like?' asked Mrs Birdlike, warming to the idea.

Sugar stared at our waitress, taking in her features, her stature, her colouring.

'Well, she had dark hair, um... blue eyes, she was quite short, she looked a lot like you.'

'Oh!' said Mrs Birdlike, clasping her hands in front of her housecoat in delight. 'It sounds like her. Did she say much? Did she mention me at all?'

'She talked a lot, she was very friendly,' said Sugar.

'Did she have a wonky eye? Our Kitty has a wonky eye.' Mrs. Birdlike peered closer at Sugar, squinting up her own eyes in disbelief.

'It was dark in the club, but I thought I detected a slight squint,' said Sugar.

'It's her! I just know it for sure. I will ring her tonight.'

Mrs Birdlike got out the pen and notebook that she kept in the front of her apron pocket, the one she used for taking down orders.

'Now, tell me again, when was this, and where?'

'Best be getting on the road, Diz,' said Sugar.

The Irish have a rare ability. They are accomplished at being able to squeeze out every last drop of information from a stranger, even if it is a lie. After confessing our full medical history, inside leg measurements and our birth weights to Mrs B, we set off again. Mrs Birdlike stood on the café steps, waving.

'What a small world it really is after all,' she called after us.

Back in the car, Sugar regained some of her previous vigour. Her face looked fresh, if not a little guilty.

'I still feel a bit sick,' she told me. 'I'll have to have my window open.'

'Serves you right! Oh, Mrs Birdlike, I know your Kitty personally. Yes, Mrs Birdlike. No, Mrs Birdlike. Three bags full of shite, Mrs Birdlike. I sometimes find it hard to believe that you went to a convent.'

Sitting in the passenger seat, with the map spread out on her lap, Sugar ignored me. She was busy attempting to navigate us safely and without incident to our first destination, Killarney.

Chapter 6

Emerald strikes again

I had been on a driving holiday before (to America, with Will, where the weather was sunny), but never have I laughed so much as on that road trip with Sugar – despite the rain. Our first driving challenge was on that very morning, when the motorway ran out of road. This happened with no warning sign, or at least not one that we noticed, so obviously we couldn't prepare for the fact that the road hadn't yet been built. We were travelling in the middle lane when it came to a rude end in front of a grey breeze block wall.

Sugar let out a peal of laughter. Her eyes filled with tears. She was absolutely no bloody help as we sat in front of the wall in Emerald, my newly acquired, lurid, green Mini.

With no choice, Emerald and I decided to navigate through the road works in the closed lane to the left of us. We nipped in between the "Road Closed" sign and the wall so we could get on our way. Not in the least bit worried that we were attempting something illegal, the fearless Emerald weaved her way through the bollards.

As we passed over the closed road, we found ourselves in the middle of a real life motorway maintenance team. We narrowly missed the tarmac roller, complete with a horrified looking driver. We tucked in behind him; a stone lorry took up our rear. We convoyed in unison with the work vehicles for three miles.

Our terrific manoeuvring skills roused a gang of men from their tea break by the side of the road. They didn't expect two girls in a Mini Clubman to be undertaking vital road resurfacing. One of the men scrambled to his feet. Still managing to hold his mug of tea, he pointed in our direction.

'Jesus, Mary and Joseph, would you look at those two, Declan.'

Declan looked up from his newspaper. Then, throwing it down to the side of him, he also rose, disbelieving, to his feet.

'You silly feckers!' he shouted.

We merely laughed and waved our way out of danger, relieved at last to have found the exit.

'Do you want me to drive, Dizzy?' asked Sugar, now with the map across her face.

'I'd love it, but you're not insured. Now shut up and read the map.' I didn't tell her I'd promised Will I wouldn't let her drive.

No harm done, we carried on with our journey. We drove on happily. It was the first day of our holiday, we didn't have a worry in the world. We screeched into Killarney by lunchtime, whereupon we did what was expected and went straight into a pub for a half pint of the black stuff, and to ask directions to the bed and breakfast.

The front of the pub had a huge window, so we could make out the mountains in the distance. Their enticing outline, framed like a picture, offered the promise of a far-off place, one that was just waiting to be discovered. I was loving Ireland already; it felt just a tiny bit like I'd gone home.

The pub seemed surprisingly crowded for a lunchtime, filled mainly by men in overalls who sat on worn red, velvet-covered bar stools, busy nursing their pints. As we walked in, all the men turned to stare at Sugar and me. Clearly, they weren't used to seeing women in a pub in the daytime.

In the main bar, the carpet was so grubby that it looked like this particular pub had been housing cattle overwinter. A pungent mid-morning smell lingered from the night before, a mix of stale beer and cigarette smoke. Quiet chat rumbled in the background.

We made our way up to the bar. The men in the pub seemed stuck in a time warp, outwardly friendly perhaps, but with a definite hint of misogyny. Luckily, we didn't have time to find out. We had to find our bed and breakfast. Sugar took control.

'Excuse me,' she said to the barman. 'Do you know where the Looneys live?' She asked this in all innocence, waving our bed and breakfast guidebook under his nose.

The barman cast his eyes up thoughtfully, looking through the window to the mountains in the distance.

'I couldn't say for sure, there's a lot of Looneys up in them hills,' he said.

We prayed he was referring to the surname, rather than the possible psychopathic tendencies of the local residents.

The Looneys lived a fair way away, by the sound of it, so we set off again. This time, we had the barman's somewhat vague directions, scribbled on the back of a beermat. As we drove higher into the hills, the lanes got narrower, and we got more and more lost. The only other life forms we witnessed were those of sheep. Sugar got quieter. We melded into the green. We became part of the scenery, our car, Emerald, now an almost invisible dot in the middle of the mountain. This was a landscape that only Heidi would find acceptable.

'Pull over Dizzy, I'm going to be sick,' said Sugar. She extracted herself from the car. Her face an unforgiving shade of sea-green blended well into the background.

'I wish I could drive,' she said.

'You have too many speeding points, remember. Frankly, my insurance company wouldn't touch you, missus,' I added.

We perched on the bumper, had a fag, admired the view. We were lost, but it didn't matter. Sugar stared ruefully at the beermat on the dashboard, which promised "Lovely day for a Guinness". She squinted her eyes to read the directions written in tiny scrawl.

'We should have turned left by the farmhouse,' she said helpfully.

'Which farmhouse?' I asked, gazing down at the scene below us, farmhouses dotted all over the landscape.

Around teatime, we found the little cream-and-green bungalow. Plastic gnomes and baskets of gaudy flowers lined the driveway, welcoming us to 'Dun Roamin' Bed and Breakfast – Vacancies.

Mr and Mrs Looney were kind. They offered us lifts, asked after our well-being like we were part of their ever-increasing family, and all within ten minutes of meeting us.

Later, we watched the Irish version of *Take the High Road* with Mammy and Dada, and the rest of the clan of Looneys. We perched on the sofa in their front room, sipping tea as if it was perfectly normal to be part of the family. So far there were eight children, but from the look of Mrs Looney's tummy, number nine wouldn't be too long before making an appearance.

Afterwards, we got a lift in Mr Looney's mustard-coloured Allegro. We were heading out to sample the Killarney delights, whilst Mr Looney was heading out to get petrol.

'What time will you be coming home now, girls?' he called, as we jumped out of the back seat of his car.

'Oh, about ten o'clock,' I lied.

'We have the key that Mrs Looney gave us,' said Sugar. 'Don't wait up.'

At one thirty in the morning we found Mr Looney had done as requested. He'd also locked us out good and proper. Unfortunately, Sugar had forgotten the key.

'Give me your coat, it's got to be in one of those pockets

somewhere,' I said, searching Sugar's long brown army surplus. 'You just haven't had a good enough look.'

'I left it in the room, I remember now,' she said.

We decided to climb in through a half-open window. Sugar started well, her head and shoulders fitting easily through the gap, but she got stuck halfway in, so, with only her front half inside, her backside hung down over the windowsill. Her legs were left dangling.

'You've eaten too much honey, Winnie,' I giggled, reaching up to heave and push at her backside. 'You'll have to stay here until you've lost weight.'

After a few more pushes, I managed to free Sugar from the window. I heard the thud as she landed safely inside the bungalow.

'You're a little Eejit and never forget it,' I called after her.

'Right,' she said. 'That's it. Why don't you go and piss off somewhere else? You're not coming in.'

As much as I pleaded, it was no use. Sugar wouldn't give in and open the front door. Unless I disturbed the Looneys, I would have no choice but to stay outside. But after some time snoozing next to the bird table on the front lawn, I was awoken, 'Dizzy! Diiiizy! Are you cold?'

Sugar was still inside the bungalow. Her silhouette framed at the window – enlarged by the huge army surplus coat and illuminated by the bedside lamp – gave the illusion that she had greatly magnified her normal outline. She dangled the front door key, but she remained firm, refusing to open the front door even when I appealed to her better nature, snatching the key out of reach as soon as I got near.

'You'll have to climb through the window, Dizzy, like I had to.'

She turned her back and walked away, the black beanie hat firmly attached to her head, its little bobble bouncing along. I watched as she got into bed, popped the key under her pillow and grinned at me. Then she reached for the pulley cord and plunged the bedroom into blackness.

'Let me in, you daft cow,' I said. 'If you don't, I'll put your beanie hat on the bird table.'

'Night, Dizzy…'

I heaved myself up at the bedroom window, clinging to the sill with my fingernails. Temporarily suspended, I desperately tried to pull myself up onto the ledge. I'm glad that Mr Looney's asleep, I thought, as I fell off the window ledge. At least he wouldn't witness me crashing into the carefully cultivated rose bushes he'd planted beneath.

It was all very silly, but by three in the morning, Sugar and I had both finally made it into our room.

CHAPTER 7

A DISCOVERY

Next day, we started the dire task of searching church records to try to find out about Marie's family. We gained some dubious information from a local man with a limp, and a horsecart driver, with no top set of teeth, who we quizzed as he drove us round Killarney Lakes. We even had a confidential chat with a priest. Then, hallelujah! It looked like we had found the correct records for the family.

By mid-afternoon we found ourselves at a graveyard near Tralee. This is where we thought some of the family were laid to rest. There we stood, two naive young girls, confronted by the imposing iron gates of the cemetery. We were astonished at the sheer number of graves, at the silent sea of grey stones spread out before us.

'We ought to split up. It'll make the job quicker. Will you be okay, Dizzy?' Sugar asked.

We both got on with our search alone. I stood in the drizzle amidst the grave stones watching Sugar in the distance. She had given up a fair chunk of her holidays to accompany me with this thankless task, using up her precious days off from the wildlife park.

The inscriptions on the graves gave me an insight into the lives of those long dead. Some of the plots were overgrown and forgotten, whilst others were well tended. Brightly coloured trinkets and mementos stood out against the starkness of the Celtic crosses. The Mary Mother of Jesus statues were like tiny candle-lit shrines.

After about an hour, Sugar beckoned me over. She was standing facing one of the stones, her head held low. Tears and rain ran down her face. She glanced up as I read out loud my natural mother's name.

*

Unable to grasp what Sugar had found, we stood in the drizzle staring in silence at the gravestone. In all my thoughts of the birth family over the past thirty years, it had never occurred to me that my mother might be dead.

Marie was only just eighteen when we twins were born. The stone inscription informed us that she had died in 1985. She would have been just thirty-five years old. Although the inscription gave no indication of her year of birth, this didn't seem particularly unusual. We had seen countless graves like this. Many of them had missing information.

I gazed across the deserted graveyard, at the hundreds of stones lined up. The silence was broken only by the occasional crow calling and the distant rumble of traffic. I decided there and then that there would be no more searching; it was all over and done with.

We drove back to Killarney in silence. The windscreen wipers swooshed and thudded their protest at the never-ending rain. Everything felt so bleak, like a Sunday afternoon in winter, not like the holiday we had imagined.

That evening, we went out to listen to a local band. We also needed to rearrange our plans for the rest of the trip. Sugar was forlorn, imagining my disappointment.

'Okay Dizzy? I'm so sorry about today darlin". Tears welled up in her eyes.

'I'm Okay, missus, thank you. You've been a star. It's a shock, but at least it's over. I can get on now.' Unlike my best friend, I had a feeling of closure on the sorry adventure. The search was over.

'But Dizzy... it's just the beginning, there could be other family out there. What about your father?'

'No, no more.'

I tried to look at anything but her beautiful face. My own tears were not far from the surface, but this was no time to be maudlin. I didn't have any interest in finding my birth father; all I had thought of was my mother. To my mind, back then, my father was never going to be in the picture.

Sugar brightened, wedging the beanie hat further down onto her head. 'Come on then, Dizzy,' she said. 'Let's get partying.'

Bless Sugar.

After about two hours, with more wine inside us, we decided to recreate a Riverdance performance down Killarney High Street. It was there that we met Tomas and Tierney. Sugar was going for a full reel, arms firmly by her side as her feet moved at speed. She had just jigged past the Irish-cum-Chinese restaurant when she crashed into Tierney.

Tierney and Tomas had been watching our tipsy Irish dancing with some amusement. Tierney leaned back against a wall, arms folded across his chest. He looked pleased with himself, a little bit smug that he had found us.

'Where are you two girls going?' he asked, laughing out loud. 'Sure Michael Flatley would love you to join him, but he's not available, so you will have to come with us.'

And what else could we do but join Tierney and his nephew Tomas for the remainder of the evening? Guinness and wine poured out of the bar as if Killarney had previously been experiencing a drought. Sunday night was live music, so we danced and jigged around the pub with some abandon. The smoking ban had just been introduced in Ireland, but we couldn't be sure that it had taken effect – it certainly hadn't in this particular pub. Every man, woman, and a few assorted hounds, just went to the ladies at the back of the pub for a smoke. The toilets had their own party going on.

Tierney, although old enough to know better, spent the next three hours trying to persuade Sugar to marry Tomas. Unfortunately, as the evening drew to a close, the drink took effect. Tierney seemed to be rapidly running out of good things to say about his nephew. In a last ditch attempt, he finally threw down his ace.

'And he isn't a mad axeman, you know. He has a lovely farmhouse.'

Sugar, bored but tipsy too, lifted her T-shirt to reveal her newly pierced belly button. Tierney's eyes widened. He straightened himself up, all the while steadying himself against the pub wall. He looked as if this was the most exciting thing that had happened to him for several years. As a fifty-something married man, it was not what he had come to expect these days in Killarney High Street.

Temporarily lost for words, he paused to take a gulp of his Guinness, his eyes all the while staring intently at Sugar's belly button. He blinked and his eyes widened further. Then, appearing to recover well from the shock of the sight of her navel – he gave a slight cough, pulled his coat down, and tried to return to his previous state, where the glimpse of a navel would be a thing of only fantasy. We were all unprepared for what he said next.

'Jesus! I'll be up all night now having a wank,' he said. He reached inside his coat pocket and produced a business card. 'Here's my phone number, in case you get into trouble.'

We decided we really should be getting on. But trying to extract ourselves wasn't easy as Tierney insisted on accompanying us to the taxi rank. As our cab drew away, we looked out of the back window at his waving figure. Standing under the street light, he persisted in blowing Sugar kisses. We threw his telephone number out of the taxi window when we were safely out of his sight.

The next day, we travelled to Limerick, staying in a bed and breakfast whose proprietor had a penchant for taxidermy. She kept a strange, but vast collection of stuffed animals. A tabby cat resided on the stairs, a poorly-looking stoat hung about in the breakfast room, while a flea-bitten fox kept guard in the porch.

We got locked into a pub till the wee, small hours, danced across the Thomond Park Bridge at dawn, and finally headed off to the Wicklow Mountains to stay with some old wildlife-park friends. After all the madness, it was good to see some familiar faces.

*

At our friends' house, it was all peat fires, good Catholic children and Avoca jumpers. Initially, we were glad of the rest. After only a few days, though, Sugar and I became bored. Staying at their remote, peaceful house up the mountain was all very well, but we were keen to do some wandering.

So, one day, in search of adventure, we wandered off. We went to explore the loch at the base of the mountain where our friends kept a small rowing boat. It was an unusually warm day, for Ireland. The water looked calm. Sugar and I decided, without our friends' permission, to take the boat out onto the water. Our mission was to try to get across the loch.

It took an hour to hoist the boat from its resting place. Then we grappled with its lead weight until we could safely manoeuvre it into the water. Whilst we toiled, the Irish weather chose to change without us noticing. We climbed triumphantly in and searched around our feet for the oars. Finally we pushed off.

We only managed to travel a few yards, no more than fifty –

still trying to find the oars – when the wind picked up. The little boat rocked and tilted in warning. Alarmed, and slightly surprised that we'd forgotten one of the oars, we took frantic turns with the remaining one. With some manic paddling, I tried to get us back to the shore. We were terrified. Amid laughter and screams, the one of us not in possession of the oar used her hands to move tiny droplets of water to aid our safe passage. The wind was crafty, though. With just a few small gusts, it succeeded in moving us further out into the loch.

I'm not sure whose idea it was to change places to help us to get to the bank more quickly, but at one point we were both standing up in the rowing boat and holding on to each other as we tried to get our pathetic selves into new positions. We failed. Both ended up facing each other, so we rearranged ourselves again. By now, the rear end of the boat was alarmingly low in the water, with both of us teetering on the same seat.

After half an hour, and a strong breeze that thankfully sent us in the correct direction, we finally reached the shore. With one last effort, Sugar crawled up the boat on her hands and knees.

'Hurry, missus! Jump on the bank! Women and children first!' I yelled.

'Dizzy, you're not so true, brave and fearless now, are you?' she called back.

It was only another hour before we had the boat back in its place on the bank. We felt totally useless. Our friend had told us that she rowed the boat as a lone adult, whilst balancing two toddlers, a baby and a golden retriever. For wildlife girls, used to dealing with all sorts, we weren't as tough as we thought.

It was during that stay with our friends, in their cottage, up on that remote mountain side, that I fell in love again. He had red hair, a naughty sense of humour and a Wicklow accent. He was called Max. He was aged three.

Sitting with the delicious Max down by the loch in the spring sunshine, I had a feeling that I ought to stop messing about working at the wildlife park. Will and I should get on with trying to have a primate of our own. I knew Will wanted children, although he never said it out loud. I didn't know how I would manage, even if Will and I were lucky enough for it to happen. But thanks to this Irish epiphany, I was, at least, willing to give it a try.

It seemed that finding out about my past had allowed me to move forward at last. Or at least that's what I hoped.

I told Will about everything when I got back home.

'Right then,' he said, 'Best we get on with it before you change your mind.'

Still, I was nervous. I knew Will would provide his usual solace – but he couldn't be pregnant for me – or give birth. These were events that you had to cope with on your own. Even Will's support, however constant and unwavering couldn't help this time. But there was a bigger more terrifying thought – what if Marie had given me away because she had had no maternal instinct? And what if I didn't have any either?

*

The day after our daughter Sasha was born, Sugar bunked off from work and hurried to the hospital. She was the first of our friends and family apart from Will to see her.

It was three days after Princess Diana's death, and some of the new mothers were crying. I couldn't be sure if it was to do with motherhood, or they were genuinely upset.

The tears I shed were not for Diana.

CHAPTER 8

A DOG CALLED TUESDAY

The autumnal days that immediately followed our daughter Sasha's birth, brought me closer to Mum and to thoughts of Marie and the horror of what she had been through when she lost her babies. Holding Sasha, feeling that she was so much a part of us, made me yet again question her decision, the circumstances that had forced her to relinquish her child. Tear after tear fell for Marie, just one of the many Irish Catholic mothers who would never properly know their children. Holding Sasha – an actual blood relative, helped to get things in perspective – it brought home to me how utterly devastating it must have been for Marie.

Sasha remained an only child. Will and I decided that we really couldn't go through another fifteen months of sleepless nights. I tried not to put her on a pedestal, but failed by over-mothering her. I was lucky; I had the pleasure, the sheer daily delight, in watching her grow. And, as we watched her turn from chubby baby into slim, leggy girl, I couldn't help wondering if she looked anything at all like Marie.

Having no memories of my birth mother, I was preoccupied

with keeping memories for Sasha, convinced that having information from her past would help nurture and develop her roots, her sense of self.

This found me keeping every newspaper clipping from her primary school achievements. I kept each one of her teeth, her first shoes, a lock of her baby blonde hair, all the wonderful pieces of art that she made.

I made countless recordings of her as she began to speak. I wanted to cling on to every bit of her young life, to record her childhood for her. That way she would never find herself wondering, there would be no gaps, she could flourish. Will had a plan of what would help keep Sasha secure.

'We just need to keep paying the rent so we can stay here,' he said. 'If we can get her to age sixteen still living in the countryside, she'll have had a good start. I had the best country childhood.'

Sasha's childhood was filled with animals, larger than life human visitors to the house, and too much laughing. It was perfectly normal for her to come back from school to find that I had taken in yet another stray, as was the case one February afternoon.

*

The dishwasher repair man eyed the greyhound suspiciously. He was kneeling down in front of, "Advanced Engineering from Germany", that was so innovative it couldn't cope with our hard West Country water.

Alarmingly for him, he was also on eye level with the latest of our canine strays, a poorly-looking, thin thing. Understandably, he was concerned.

'So you found him in your barn this morning then?' he asked, his voice becoming muffled as he half climbed into the wash compartment wielding a spanner.

'I reckon he's a traveller's dog. You going to put that muzzle back on him when he's had his breakfast?' he continued.

'Yes, we don't know what he's like yet, I suppose,' I said.

I fussed over our new arrival, gently stroking his red fur, then slipped the muzzle back on, taking the opportunity to have a look at his horrid, yellowing teeth.

'What shall we call him?' I mused aloud, while making tea for the dishwasher man.

'Tuesday? It's Tuesday today.'

'No – that's a daft name,' I said.

'Well, whatever his name is, he doesn't smell very special.'

I wrestled Tuesday into the bath. He looked a sorry state when dry, but once wet the poorness of his condition was evident. Tuesday had obviously never had a bath before but, as I scrubbed at his flea-bitten coat, he hung his head, tucking it under my armpit, relaxing slightly as the warm water warmed his bones. Bones that protruded, especially around his shoulder blades and rear end. He was at least a stone underweight. Exhausted after his bath, he collapsed on an old duvet next to a radiator and proceeded to sleep for a full eight hours. Clearly, he'd been straying for some time.

We fed him scrambled egg, but his stomach just wasn't used to meals made in a kitchen. His previous diet had probably been vermin-based, so he immediately brought the whole sorry egg mixture back up.

By teatime, his flatulence had us evacuating the house. We stood in the porch, watching the sleet falling outside. I shuddered. I had smelt some dire concoctions when I worked at the wildlife park, but this surpassed anything we had sniffed before. We decided that his worrying windiness would need investigation from a vet.

The next day, Sighthound Rescue came and went. They were full of helpful advice. They could take Tuesday now if we didn't want him, but he would have to go into a kennel until he could be assessed, then fostered into a home. Fostered? No dog of mine was going to be fostered.

'If you could, say, hang onto him for three weeks, until a space becomes available, then one of our homes will have a vacancy,' Minty the volunteer told us. 'We'll do all we can to help. After all, you didn't really expect to find a stray on your farm did you?'

It was a bitter February day; we couldn't send Tuesday to a kennel. So, we battled on. But over the next few weeks, it become apparent that we had taken on a big red dog that had no social skills, no training and definitely no manners. Tuesday had some pretty wayward habits. The trouble was, by then, we had fallen in love with him.

It seemed that his unpredictable behaviour stemmed from his fear, so we set about a programme of dog training classes. As we drove to the village hall where his education would begin, Tuesday was hot and panting. He licked the car window for the entire journey and raged at every passing dog, cat or car. When he saw a push bike, he went into a frenzy.

All things were strange to him: stairs, men with hats, collars and leads, vacuum cleaners, eating out of a dish, being loved. He was a puppy in an eighteen-month-old body with an aggressive attitude – a liability. It wasn't his fault. But as my mum had made clear in one of her letters, 'You mustn't carry on with such a chancy dog'. And as she kept reminding me with her endless follow up phone calls, 'I'm not interfering, love, but I do think Tuesday will have to sharpen up, or go to the kennel.'

Unfortunately, we managed to arrive at the village hall at the exact moment the local rugby team chose to jog out of their changing room for practice. This was too much for Tuesday, he tried to take off after them.

It took a while to unravel ourselves; in the end, neither of us knew who was leading who. I steered Tuesday through the door to the dog training class, but the sight of the other dogs and the associated barking did little for his, or my, mental health.

We walked in past the small serving hatch where scary dog women stood in a group, gossiping. They all seemed to be wearing the latest in blue body warmers, cream neck scarves decorated with red Scottie dogs, and brown corduroy trousers. Unsmiling, and as one, they dished out tea without sympathy. I smiled, trying to look in control, then gave my name and the registration fee, taking my eye off Tuesday for just five seconds. That was enough time to give him the chance to spot the plate of biscuits. Taking advantage of his long legs, he leaned over the hatch and gulped the lot. The obedience training women stared but made no comment.

Our first training exercise was to walk round the room, get to a certain point and make our beloved canines sit. A task that all the other dogs and owners in the room did with ease. Tuesday had other ideas. He didn't know how to sit, he didn't even know his name. In fact, I think he had forgotten which planet he was on.

We set off with a determined stride, getting in a few steps before we turned. By this point, Tuesday was straining to be at the very end of the lead that restrained him. In just a few seconds, and completely unexpectedly, he managed to bite a well-behaved black labrador called Dillon, which had been lolloping innocently ahead of us. Tuesday had Dillon by the throat and wasn't letting go. The group of dog women leapt to the rescue. They must have had training, because their rapid response was exemplary.

We were ushered away from the scene of the crime to sit in the corner and take time out to think about our actions. Dillon's owner was pacified with a chocolate digestive. To be fair, Dillon didn't seem bothered; he just snuffled his nose along the floor hoping for a crumb of food, letting out the odd fart. Maybe his labrador brain hadn't registered what had taken place.

By now, I had Tuesday in such a tight grip that I wondered if I was restricting his airway. I told him that biting Dillons wasn't allowed, even if they did look like they were one Bonio short of a packet. 'And you really mustn't eat the tea-break biscuits,' I said 'at least, not unless they're bone shaped.' Tuesday gave my hand a lick. It was difficult to be cross for long.

The not-so-sympathetic trainer stomped over and declared,

'There's no hope for Tuesday, join the class near Bristol, for Damaged Dogs. You'll never do anything with that Greyhound, it's too late for him.'

Tuesday was still young, so I disagreed, but as he wasn't welcome here we made our excuses. We began the recommended one-to-one classes for damaged dogs, even though it was like taking Tuesday to probation. We even thought they were starting to pay off. Unfortunately for us, though, he had merely been lulling us into a false sense of security. His next trick was to jump over the garden gate, effortlessly landing on a bloke who was innocently pedalling by on a push bike, knocking him to the ground before lying on top of him so he couldn't escape. We heard the screams from inside the house and we rushed out to rescue the cyclist from Tuesday's grip. A Band Aid, a cup of tea and an apology later, found the furious man sitting on a garden chair while I bustled about unsure of what to do.

'That dog's dangerous. Look at my hand,' he said.

He held up his left arm where the graze looked raw and weeping.

'I'm very sorry, we've only had him a few weeks. He was a stray.'

'I'm not surprised he was a stray. You should watch him with your little girl, he's not safe. Take my advice and get rid of him.'

'I don't think he bit you, did he?' I asked. 'That graze is from where you fell off the bike.'

'No, he bit me, he's nasty. Anyway, I wouldn't have bloody well fallen off the bike if he hadn't landed on me. It's enough to give someone a heart attack.'

Even though Tuesday regularly nipped friends and family, he never so much as lifted his lip at us. Still, with his recent victims playing heavily on our minds, we used a muzzle when Tuesday was outside and, as an emergency measure, I rigged up electric horse fencing to keep our spirited friend confined to quarters.

Tuesday never got a shock from the fence. He learned to

limbo underneath. We, on the other hand, were electrified on an almost daily basis, if in a hurry, we forgot to turn off the battery. It was just as well that he never got a shock from the fence as, underneath his bravado, Tuesday wasn't very brave – the smallest amount of pain, even a stubbed toe for instance, resulted in him taking bed rest to recover.

Will began walking him at six thirty in the morning so he didn't meet other dogs, but Tuesday wasn't happy at being evicted from his slumbers at such an early hour. We knew it wasn't helping Tuesday by allowing him upstairs, but at least we knew what he was up to – especially as he was an accomplished food thief.

If he was in trouble, like the day he stole the bacon, he would sulk off upstairs to his duvet and pretend to be dead. He could lie very still and just move his eyes. On this particular day, he moved his eyes left to look at the bacon, shifted them right at me, then shut them tightly.

'Don't disturb him, Mummy. Tuesday's pretending to be asleep.'

'Thank you, Sash. Yes, let's leave him to it.'

Tuesday's favourite victim was a sales rep we nicknamed Bernard Bullshit. Bernard, large and jolly, made twice-weekly visits to the forge that Will ran from the farm. He tried over and again to become pals with our dog, we'd often find Bernard chatting to him through the fence, but Tuesday would not let down his guard.

'Oh, you're a good boy. I love dogs, come here fellow,' he whispered.

It gave me the willies seeing his persistence: Bernard was going to get it, it was only a matter of time. Tuesday had memorised Bernard's blue van. Emblazoned on both sides was "METALWORK SUPPLIES, ABSOLUTELY NO BULLSHIT, GUARANTEED".

Keeping watch on Monday and Thursday lunchtimes, he would lie in wait for Bernard. As soon as he heard the familiar sound of the engine and the two beep beeps that signalled his arrival, Tuesday was off round the perimeter of the garden, looking for a way out, growling for the duration of Bernard's visit.

One day, I forgot to put on the electric fence. I was upstairs when I noticed that Tuesday had escaped – he was lurking about in the field beyond the garden, partly concealed by the long grass, sniffing for mice in the hedgerows. But, unfortunately for Bernard, as soon as he heard the Bedford van's horn he appeared – huge on the horizon like a beast. He started running full pelt back towards the driveway. I could see him approaching but was powerless to get to Bernard in time.

'TUESDAY, NO!' I yelled out of the bedroom window. 'BERNARD, QUICKLY, GO THROUGH THE GATE.'

But Tuesday was gaining.

'WILL… HELP! SAVE BERNARD…'

Bernard moved with some speed – which was unusual, given his size – but, too fat to run, he powered his short legs up the little garden path with Tuesday thundering down the driveway towards him. Just as Bernard pushed the metal catch shut behind him, Tuesday flung himself at the gate, then leapt up and nipped his finger. Will appeared out of the workshop and he too started running up the path.

I rushed out of the house. Now Tuesday was leaping up and down at the gate – he seemed to be getting higher with every one of his attempts to try to get over, and poor Bernard was trapped in the garden.

'Did he bite you Bernard?'

'No, gorgeous. He just licked me, he's fine.'

'I'm so sorry, Bernard,' said Will, grabbing hold of Tuesday's collar. 'I'll put him in the house.'

Tuesday and I both stared at Bernard's podgy, pink finger as it started to swell and look like a fat chipolata. We watched, horrified, as his large, ungainly body wobbled back to the van.

I gave him some chicken's eggs as way of admitting liability.

The hens had the measure of him, always flocking around his van as he gave them bits of his sandwiches. They, at least, were Bernard's friends.

We ordered dog training DVDs, but Tuesday refused to watch them. We tried clicker training, but it sent him into a deep depression.

Will decided that greyhounds needed a softer approach. So began the long and lonely rehab path. Meanwhile, our greyhound was getting a reputation. The local postman had reported Tuesday to the postmaster. The GPO declared the dog was "unreliable" and that post would be left in the forge.

*

Tuesday was proving too much for even the most committed dog lover. Over the next few months nothing changed so I phoned the ever-patient Minty.

'He's not the correct dog for you, Dizzy. Let us have him back. Could you drop him at the kennels tomorrow morning? Don't worry, you've done well.'

All night long we hugged Tuesday close. He snuggled ever nearer, between us in our bed, his head resting on the pillow next to Will's. This was his last night in our home.

In the early morning, we packed up his blankets, coats, and food.

Five-year-old Sasha couldn't understand why her best friend had to go and live somewhere else. 'No,' we explained, 'we won't be able to visit him – it's heartbreaking, but it's the best thing for Tuesday.'

To the rescue came the long-suffering, ever supportive, Will.

'I don't think we ought to give up on him. We made a commitment, he shouldn't be pushed from pillar to post. It'll be awful for him to go to another home, and I can't bear it. Let's keep him, Diz: he can't get any worse.'

Unaware of the grief we humans were going through, Tuesday took up his position on the sofa. Between naps, he watched daytime TV, gaining useful recipe ideas along the way, soothed by Lorraine Kelly. My mother arrived later that morning with one of her advice notes, a shepherd's pie, and a clear plastic bag of grated cheese for the topping.

'I'm sure you don't feel like cooking after all the upset, love,' she called through the porch door to me.

She hadn't taken more than one step inside when Tuesday was up and on his feet. He snatched the grated cheese, devoured the contents, then finished off the bag. Horrified, we witnessed the last of the clear plastic being sucked in through his large grubby teeth.

'I don't know why you carry on with that dog, Dizzy. What's his name? Tuesday? You should call him Merlin. He was certainly a wizard to find you.'

'He can't help it, Mum; look at those scars. The vet thinks he was shot with an air rifle in the past.'

Mum's resolve weakened and she held out her hand to Tuesday by way of apology. Effortlessly, he lifted his front legs to rest them on her shoulders, licking her face in the hope of finding a crumb. I steadied mum as she fell back against the wall, not tall enough to be hugged by a long, lean dog.

'You're too soft, my girl,' she said, straightening herself up, trying to regain her composure. 'Still, I suppose you were a stray, and we're glad we kept you.'

Her words hit home. I realised then, that was why I was battling on with Tuesday; it was because nobody else wanted him.

From that day forward, Tuesday was renamed Merlin. I knew I could never part with him. We both had a hint of the unconventional, an angry attitude, an uncertain past. We understood each other perfectly.

CHAPTER 9

MEETING TOMMY

Sometimes, extraordinary events take place on ordinary days. On this particular day, all seemed normal. From the forge came the clatter of hammers, punctuated by occasional cussing and swearing as Will and Nathan the "apprentice" wrestled with huge chunks of steel. Nathan had obviously dropped something, because I heard an awful crash, 'For pity's sake, Nathan, were you born yesterday?' Will said… then silence.

On this particular day, we found ourselves outside – the weather wouldn't allow Merlin and me to stay indoors – and it wasn't long before I was staring through the open forge door. The temperature inside the building couldn't be contained within the walls of the old milking parlour, it hit me – along with the deadening thud of the power hammer. The terrible working conditions – the daily physical grind – meant blacksmithing was becoming a dying art.

Will, bent double over the anvil, wiped the sweat from his eyes with his sleeve. He scraped a wire brush along a bar to remove the scale that had formed as it was heated. This bar was one of the many hundreds of railings that Will was making for a heritage project. This particular labour would take him eighteen months, and pave the way for changes in our lives which were as yet unseen.

I watched as Will plunged the bar into the fire and waited for it to turn from red to white, the colour he needed to fire weld it. Normally, the fire only needed to heat up the metal to scarlet. Most techniques could be achieved at this colour stage. Will had told me that once it reached the required white hot state there was only about thirty seconds when the metal was malleable. He said that you had only three attempts, the bar started to weaken after the first heat.

I watched as he took the bar to the forge, then quickly back to the anvil, where he brought it to life. It sparked its objection – now at its most vulnerable – as the fire had denatured its structure, turning it from red to yellow to defenceless white. The sulphate the bar released as it changed smelled of onions, rather than the normal musty odour reminiscent of domestic coal fires and what I witnessed certainly wasn't a cosy homespun scene. Staring through the door into the forge was like looking into a bygone era. The environment for Will's working world seemed, to me, to belong to a different century, more like the early 1800s – rather than 2004.

With Sasha now at school I had more time. I was engaged in more gentle pursuits than Will, including the office work needed to support the forge; practical matters, like getting our new business line installed; and daily domestic chores, like the laundry.

Leaving Will to his labours, I returned to the house, piled the newly-done washing into a basket and went out again. Merlin pounced about the garden, trying to uncover the voles and mice that nested in enticing places, just out of reach. I pegged out the assortment of clothes: Sasha's blue school uniform, work overalls that didn't look much cleaner, a red woollen dog blanket and twenty pairs of black socks.

We had the best view from any washing line I'd ever seen; it overlooked the tract of an old hill fort. My eyes stretched up to the site.

Although the fort had crumbled into the soil years before, the mound of earth was etched with faint horizontal lines, almost invisible, ingrained just beneath the grass, giving a clue to the plough lines of the past. Ley lines ran across that land, too, unseen, unchanging, hidden beneath the modern day veneer of farming.

I planned the day ahead, which included a few jobs for the business, booking the holiday offer I had seen the night before, and thinking about Merlin's dog training class that evening – though, of course, I didn't expect that to go very well.

I heard the postman's van push the gravel further into the impacted soil as he careered down the drive and watched as he rolled down the window and handed Will a bundle of letters. These days, Kevin, the latest and most dog-wary of our postmen, didn't get out of the van – Merlin had developed a particular dislike of him.

I finished with the washing and went to collect the post. I was expecting a letter from my mum. Her advice notes were legendary. We hadn't received one for a couple of weeks, not since a disagreement a few weekends back involving the tricky subject of MMR childhood vaccinations. A note was bound to be wending its way by now. Mum used assorted communications to get her point across to me, face-to-face chats, phone calls, but sometimes she preferred to write her feelings down, rather than saying them out loud.

So, I really wasn't expecting to receive a letter from social services that June morning – certainly not one that said someone was looking for me. It was carefully worded in case, I suppose, it fell into the wrong hands, but it didn't take long for me to realise that it related to my adoption. Why now after all these years? – I was thirty-six years old. I was at a loss to know what to do. Sugar was at work, so I did what any girl would; I rang my mum.

'Mum? There's a letter, it arrived ten minutes ago. It's from social services saying someone wants to contact me.'

'Oh my goodness, Dizzy.'

The first tears of many were waiting and I could no longer hold them back.

'It's okay, Diz, now don't go upsetting yourself, my love, take your time. But do you think it's your mother?' she asked.

'Well, no, I found that grave, remember?'

'Well, that could have been wrong.'

Mum had to wait for my reply. Unable to master the emotion, I couldn't get the words out. 'No, it'll be my father. I have a feeling.'

There was a pause, just long enough for the love to dart up the phone line between me and my mum.

'Would you like me to come over, love?'

'No, no, I'm meant to be doing jobs for the business.'

'Well, I'm sure they can wait until tomorrow.'

'Yes, they can, but don't come over. I just need to be on my own for a bit. Are you all right about this, Mum? It must be a terrible shock for you too.'

'Oh love, I'm pleased for you.' I could hear tears now behind her words. 'I never expected it, but I'm curious. I bet it's your mum, Dizzy.'

'You're my mum.'

'I don't mind, nothing can take away what we have. I love you and Ellis more than anything. If this helps make sense of the past it's a good thing. If you and your brother are all right, I'm all right.'

This was typical of our mum; she always put herself last.

'I wasn't looking anymore, Mum. This isn't my choice. I don't need any other parent but you.'

I later realised, with the benefit of hindsight, that surely anyone would want to find out, once they'd received such a letter. But, although it was shocking to receive the news, it was also the start of the most exciting journey – like falling in love. Those first moments when you find out about the other person, hanging onto any glimpse of a spark of similarity.

My priority now was to make contact with social services. But everything moved slowly. It took three days to get an actual phone conversation arranged with the social worker. Three long days, during which I paced the floorboards. But finally the phone call came and Lyn, the social worker, explained to me that it was my father Tommy who had been going to a fair bit of effort to track me down.

I wasn't given Tommy's email address or any contact information directly. I was, however, given the number of a private detective that my father had hired. The detective, Emma, was to be the go-between. Emails, then letters, sped between home, Emma and the Middle East where my birth father was spending three months.

I fell upon the first email she sent me from Tommy. After all the years of wondering, to at last have some correspondence, to have a glimpse into his character, was staggering. Speculation would soon be a thing of the past.

Emma kept a rein on events, slowing down our correspondence so we could take it all in, but Tommy and I just couldn't get enough information about each other. After about two months, a little nervously, we decided to exchange email addresses. Without Emma's eyes to steady our relationship, we felt released from constraint. With our new-found freedom, we wrote emails almost daily. Tommy had a lot to write about; he'd had a jam-packed life, achieving more than most. It was wonderful getting to know him.

And then, at last, the long-awaited phone call came in the early autumn. It was with a mixture of surprise and gritty reality that I heard his voice for the first time. As a Yorkshire man, he had a way of speaking that could come across as abrupt. When I asked anything from him or tried to get clarity, he punctuated sentences with remarks such as "of course" or "obviously". When I didn't understand his explanations, it made me feel stupid to have to ask again. Consequently, I was left without many of the answers.

'I won't tell you all of the information about your past right away,' he said. Remarks like this led me to believe that Tommy was trying to control the situation.

Looking back now, through kinder eyes, I'm sure he was trying to shield us both. He did tell me, though, during one of our first phone calls, that he'd really loved my mother and that they were together for eighteen months – engaged, even.

'You weren't the result of a fumble down a back alley,' Tommy explained.

'What happened, then?' I asked him.

'I was young, and I chose the Army over your mother. But, I never stopped thinking about you both. It was whilst I was posted out in the Falkland Islands, during the conflict, that I knew I would have to find Marie. And you,' Tommy said. 'You see, I met this ornithologist on the island. It was just the two of us there, waiting it out. We had some deep talks about life, like you do in those sort of situations. She told me she never knew her father; it was after talking to her that I decided to start the search one day. I had never seen you or your twin. I regret my actions, the way I treated your mother. I let her down badly.'

He sent photographs from his album so that we could piece together the family tree. He also posted to us various newspaper clippings, one telling of his adventure dry-skiing, from Lands End to John O'Groats to raise money for charity.

Sure enough, the photos and newspaper articles made sense of his many achievements. It was becoming apparent that Tommy had had quite a life, including a long career in the Forces, then training to be a social worker. He had gained three degrees – probably during his spare time – and he was writing a book. His hobbies included open water swimming, coaching young people in sports, and travelling the world. He had several children. The precise number would be revealed at a later date.

Tommy phoned weekly; we weren't like father and daughter, but nevertheless, we were becoming friends. Still, I had a longing for him to step up to the mark, for him to give me some fatherly advice for one of the many dilemmas we faced. These included dog behaviour.

'Take him out running. Get on your bike, chuck, you need to wear that dog of yours out.'

As the months wore on, it was natural to want to meet up. Tommy wasn't backward in coming forward on the arrangements front, but I had my reservations.

'When we finally meet, do you want it to be at your twin sister's grave?' he asked. 'I want to go there anyway.'

'No, it's too much, that's not the place. If I want to go there, I'll do it alone,' I said.

'Well, suit yourself, but I want to meet you as soon as possible – when you're ready, of course.'

So, that October, Will and I met Tommy near Bristol.

'I want to hold your hand, chuck,' he told me.

I'd got ready for some big occasions before, but so far nothing had topped this. We saw him as we nervously entered the pub. He was walking across the room towards us, hand outstretched. He was very smartly turned out, wearing a shirt and tie.

I sat opposite Tommy so that I could soak in every last one of his features. My first impressions were of a gentle, kind man. He answered our many questions as best he could. All the time, Tommy's pale blue eyes watched us carefully.

We talked about Sasha. 'I understand why you don't want to confuse her with introducing me at this stage,' he said. And I couldn't talk about Marie, or ask anything about her, because Tommy had his wife with him.

We hugged and had our photos taken outside in the car park, as you would on such an astonishing occasion. Another one for the family album, I thought.

As we drove home, it was Will who broke the silence. 'There are no family resemblances between you and Tommy, Diz –

nothing similar about the two of you, except you both turned up and put your diaries on the table before sitting down. That's hardly a genetic link; I don't think he's your father.'

I cast Will a suspicious glance; it had all been enough to take in without now thinking we had the wrong fellow.

'Mind you,' Will went on, 'he was smartly dressed. That's his Army background, I expect. He seems a decent bloke, but I don't believe he's anything to do with you.'

So, over the next few weeks, I kept correspondence with Tommy, but in the back of my mind I wondered if what Will had said could be right. Perhaps Tommy wasn't really my genetic father after all, but with no mother to ask I would never know.

All went quiet. We tried to return to some sort of normality. It was a relief to have got the whole episode cerebrated. I didn't realise then that this was just the start of things, that more of a shock was to follow.

The fire was lit and the dogs were snoozing away their autumnal evening on another of those ordinary days. It was Saturday; I'm sure *X Factor* had just started on the TV. I heard the phone ring. When I answered it was Tommy's voice that I heard at the other end of the line.

'All right, chuck? Thought I'd give you a ring. Are you busy?'

'No...'

'Good, because I'm outside a bar in Sheffield and inside is your birth mother.'

Completely astounded, I couldn't take in the news.

'What! But I thought she was dead...'

'No chuck, she's alive and well. D'you want to speak to her?'

'No, Christ... no.'

'Your sisters are here as well.'

'Sisters? There are sisters?'

I repeated the word to myself; if I said it again, it might sink in.

'You have three half-siblings from Marie. Two sisters and one brother.'

'I already have a brother,' I replied.

This was getting serious; tummy butterflies that were normally cocooned hatched simultaneously; they went into a flying fit, free-falling towards my feet. Instead of feeling pleased with the startling news, I was horrified – another side of the family might want to be met. We might have to go through the whole darn thing again!

At that moment, all I could think of was that they might just appear, they could all suddenly arrive on the doorstep.

'Have you told them where we live?' I asked.

'No, of course not.'

But panic made fun of rational thought. Feelings overwhelmed me, feelings that told me not to believe him. After all, Tommy had kept my mother's identity a mystery over the past few months, when all along he knew she was alive, so I wasn't sure I should trust him. With Marie back from the dead, I began to wonder if it had been easier on my mind when I thought she'd passed over to the other side.

'I expect this news is a bit of a shock,' Tommy said, 'but I didn't want to bombard you with it all when you and I first started corresponding.'

'A shock, yes.'

I put down the handset, and stared at it for a few moments, then I lifted it up once more, then replaced it again so I could listen for the click, making sure I was disconnected. I could hear Will, in the next room, the kitchen. He was standing with his back to the Rayburn, the oven door open, warming himself.

'Dizzy, love,' he said, 'what are you going to do?'

'Not tell Sasha yet, it's too much, isn't it? I can't even get my head round it, so how could Sasha begin to understand?'

'Yes,' said Will. 'I heard you talking to Tommy. You must ring your mum in the morning – you must tell her.'

'Well, of course.'

'I thought we were getting to the end of all this,' Will said. 'Are you sure you're ready? Are you going to contact Marie?'

'I don't see I have much choice. You must be getting fed up with it all,' I replied. 'You've been very patient.'

'I've tried to see why it's so important, and it was probably my fault you went looking in the first place,' he said, 'but it's taken such a toll on us all; it's been all-consuming for months, hasn't it? I mean, I just wish it was all over.'

'Will, I've spent years thinking Marie was dead.'

'Yes, I see all that. But you have a wonderful mum, and stepdad; you have Ellis, me, and Sasha. Are we not enough?' he asked.

'It's not about all of you not being enough. I thought you understood why it's so important, but perhaps nobody can get that. I'm just asking, please, that you give me a bit longer, then we can get back to normal.'

That night I expected sleep not to be forthcoming. There was no point in keeping Will up, and I didn't feel like getting in bed with him after our disagreement. I preferred Merlin's company; he understood. So, I decamped to the spare room where my dog was waiting. He would be my protector should any strange relations turn up at the house. Tommy's phone call had messed everything up. The news of Marie's reappearance was a situation that left us feeling out of control. I tried to breathe away the fear – but the empty feeling that lingered in the pit of my stomach would not dissipate.

'If the Sheffield lot turn up, you're to get them by the ankles – if I shout BURGLAR that's your clue,' I told Merlin as we snuggled down under the duvet together. He rested his head on the pillow next to mine and let out a dog-tired sigh; eyes tight shut, he drifted off.

That night, my dreams had to be re-arranged. Now that I knew Marie was alive, I began once more to imagine the mother that I'd never met.

Chapter 10

Scared of My Own Shadow

First thing on the following Monday morning, I shut myself into the office and contacted Lyn the social worker.

'You need to feel in control over this,' she said. 'It must be very upsetting for you, Dizzy, but it's all too common, unfortunately, for things to get out of hand, to move too quickly in situations such as yours. My advice would be to email Tommy to tell him how you feel.'

'Yes, you're right. Thank you so much, you've been such a help. I can't imagine what Marie must be feeling, though, waiting to hear back after all this time. I feel like I should get in contact.'

'Quite, but you need to do this in your own time.'

I sent a brief, but somewhat cold email to Tommy.

Hello Tommy,

I'm writing to Marie today. I will post the letter to you, so you can forward it to her as you have her address. Send the letter on to her straight away would you please? It isn't

my intention to make her feel ignored – Marie has waited long enough!
Kind regards,
Dizzy

Even if I hadn't wanted to contact Marie, it felt like there was little option now. But there was another, more pivotal person to contact first. I phoned my mum, again… I had to tell Paula that Marie was alive.

'So, you're saying that Tommy was actually with her when he rang you – that Tommy has known all along that Marie was alive?' she asked.

'Yes – and my two half sisters were there as well.'

'You have sisters? I don't know what to make of it – it's all very strange, Dizzy. Are you going to contact Marie?'

'If you don't mind, Mum, then yes.'

'Poor woman – what a shock for everyone. If that was me, I would be going out of my mind with worry. She surely wants to hear from you. You must write to her – that can't hurt, can it?'

There was an important letter to write. The question was how to begin such a task.

6th November 2004

Dear Marie,

It's hard to know where to begin with all this. What a shock for both of us then, to find out about each other, and in such a bizarre way. It's a lot to cope with for the whole family.

I have always wondered about you and what happened. It all seemed too much to find out the way I did the other evening, when Tommy phoned me from outside the pub. I have asked him to pass on the social worker's number to you, as surely, she is the best person for the job.

I have always thought such a lot about you, so much so that I put my details on the birth contact register in case you were out there. I wasn't surprised, though, when we heard nothing back. Two years before, in 1996, when I had no real information to go on, I went with a friend to Ireland to do some research. We were careful not to contact anybody there. We went to churches to look at the records and I thought we had found the correct family. It was when we were looking around a graveyard near Tralee that we found a grave with your name on it. Without the birth date on the grave we could not be sure it was you, but I wrongly assumed that it was. So, until the day before yesterday, on Saturday night, when Tommy rang, I thought that you had died.

I have always felt sorry for the circumstances you found yourself in back in 1968, and have felt that you did the most unselfish thing by putting me up for adoption. I have had a good life, with wonderful family in a secure and loving home. My adoptive parents, Paula and Terry, never made any secret about the adoption; my dad, Terry, was adopted when he was five-years-old, from a Dr Barnardo's home, so adoption is something our family has always been comfortable with.

They told me all they knew about you: that you were an Irish Catholic girl – you didn't want to give me up but had no real choice. Until we received the birth file, I didn't realise that, when we entered this world, even though only twenty minutes apart, we twins were born on different days.

My parents already had their own son, Ellis, ten years my senior. They couldn't have any more children, so, for them to have the chance of another child has been a wonderful thing. Our nan lived with us and helped a lot in bringing up me and my brother, Ellis. She was an extra mum to us. So you see, I went to a wonderful family.

It must be hard for you to read this, but it's not my intention to upset you, just to explain that it's all right and to hope you take some comfort in that. I'm sure you have wondered. I now live in the countryside in Somerset with my partner, Will. We have been together for seventeen years. We have one daughter, but we have had no more children. Paula and Terry, my parents, are divorced now; neither are at all worried about you or Tommy coming along. We are all secure enough to know that it won't affect the way we feel about each other, it's a positive thing that you and Tommy are there.

I never expected to find out about either of you. I treasure the photos that I have of Tommy – photos are something I longed for when I was growing up.

It is with an open heart that I send this letter to you; I would love a reply, if you feel able. If it is all too much, just see how you go.

Take care, Marie,
Dizzy

By early afternoon, Merlin and I found ourselves wandering up the narrow lane, the one that runs alongside the wood, just up the little hill behind the house. We were going to post my letter. Merlin padded almost silently beside me. The only sounds were the metal tassels clinking against the buckle of his thick greyhound collar. He stood patiently by my side at the post box as I fretted, turning over the envelope that contained the letter for Marie, pushing it through the slot just in time to catch the afternoon collection by Kevin, our terrified postman. But it was some time before proper correspondence began.

Initially, I was overconfident, certain in the knowledge that I would hear back within a few days, even though I'd said that I understood if she didn't reply, and even though I was telling myself over and over again that she probably wouldn't.

Soon though, I was desperate for a letter. Unbeknown to us, it took Tommy ten days to pass the letter on. Ten intervening days during which time hung heavy. Will, Mum and I felt for Marie, not wanting her to go through any more anguish, but we couldn't understand why I had heard nothing back.

Eventually, I'd had enough. One evening, I prepared to shut myself in the office again, but this time I wouldn't email Tommy, I was going to ring and ask directly whether he'd passed the letter on. Ready to confront him – ready to engage in yet another epic phone call. The average length of the phone calls to my birth family were as long as most films. So, as I disappeared into the office, for 'another chat', armed with yet another cup of tea and a tin full of tiny roll ups, Will informed me that he was preparing to entertain himself from his impressive back catalogue of film classics.

'What are you watching tonight?' I asked.

'*Zulu*.'

Once on the phone, Tommy was quick to explain. 'I was just giving you some time, I wasn't sure it was right for you, so I didn't post the letter to Marie for a few days. I'm sure this has all been a bit much, chuck.'

'Thank you,' I replied. 'That's true enough, but it's our choice now. I'm thirty-six years old and Marie is fifty-four. It's up to us. I reckon we're both old enough to handle it, and she must have been waiting for a letter.'

'I've been trying to protect you. I'm aware of how hard it's been. I've started a drama for you all.'

'It's too late for regret now,' I said.

'I've no regret for finding your mother, or you. I only regret having treated her so badly. You see, I thought if I managed to get the two of you back together, it would go some way to making it up to Marie.'

CHAPTER 11

EVERYONE LOOKS THE SAME

She finally wrote back. Her first letter wasn't brief. It contained photographs of her family, slipped between the sheets of notepaper. I tried to follow Lyn's advice to take things at a steadier pace, so this time round it was less frenetic than when I'd first corresponded with Tommy, but it was no less engulfing. What should have been the oldest relationship was the newest one. It felt more important to get it right.

So that late December morning, when the postman arrived bearing an envelope containing Marie's letter and photos of her and her family – well, that was just the start. I had anticipated that her letter would arrive any day. In fact, since Tommy's phone call, I'd been awake half of the intervening nights. Merlin and I had been trying to get a hold on our anxieties without much success. This time I found myself worrying I would forget what it was like not knowing! The sepia pictures that fell out of the envelope did not change that feeling.

Not knowing was having unfilled spaces, like a piece of Swiss cheese. I was used to them, the spaces; they represented gaps in my life I had long known were there. They were what I had grown up with. I had spent over thirty years filling in the gaps with images of a whole world of people who acted out their lives in my imagination.

The big brown outer envelope had come via social services, because Marie didn't know where we lived. Inside, was a note from Lyn.

> *Dear Dervla,*
>
> *I hope you are well and are not finding this all too overwhelming. Marie contacted me to thank you for the sensitivity of your letter. Here is her reply and photos.*
>
> *Contact me when you are ready!*

The envelope was standard social services issue, but the smaller envelope inside was a personal choice, creamy yellow in colour. Spidery handwriting in black ink scuttled across it.

> *Sheffield, December 2004*
>
> *Dear Dervla,*
>
> *Thank you for your lovely letter. I'm so glad that you wanted and looked forward to hearing back from me. It's the same for me. I couldn't wait to get your first letter. I had a feeling you would write to me. I was even stopping the postman lately, in the mornings, waiting for your letter to come.*
>
> *I think about you all the time, as I always have. Birthdays and Christmases have in the past been the worst times, especially when you were growing up. I constantly wondered what your face was like when you opened your presents.*
>
> *I used to look at my other children, and sometimes I could see you when you were born. You were a little scrap of a thing, so tiny and beautiful. When I heard you cry for*

the first time it was the most wonderful feeling, as I'm sure you know, being a mum yourself.

You looked like Tommy when you were born, but by the photographs I have of you, that Tommy gave me, you resemble me now, very much so.

My life, Dervla, has not been easy, but I am strong now. So many bumps in life does that for you. I've never been a bitter person. People that know me say I have a very soft heart, I'm glad about that.

Carla cried when we got your letter. Helena and Patrick are wanting to meet you.

I ought to tell you about my parents, you need to know what happened. Initially, they came over to England from Ireland for a visit, they stayed with my mother's sister and her husband. Apparently, there was a big falling out and my uncle and aunt kept hold of us children, but threw my parents out on the streets. My mother and father had to go back to Ireland without us. I never went back to Ireland with them. I lived with my aunt after that, she brought me up. My brothers Aedan and Rory were also in England, but we were eventually separated.

My real mother says we were stolen from her and my father. I remember my father coming to our house to visit me. These were the times, he told me later, that he came to try to bring me back. It never happened.

My aunt told me we were left. I don't suppose I'll ever know the truth, but my parents stayed married and had the other children. My aunt was capable of all the things my mother told me about and I knew my mother was speaking honestly. She was twenty, and my father was twenty-two when they had me. Telling you these things is not meant to make you feel sad. Just so you can maybe get a picture of the past.

Dervla, would you mind if I sent a present to your daughter? A Christmas present. Please say if you think this is a bad idea. I understand. I expect she still believes in Santa, so she wouldn't need to know it's from me. See how you feel. I won't be offended if you're not comfortable with it.

I hope to hear from you soon.

All my love,

Marie

xx

I pulled out the photographs, which were worn around the edges. Before me were nephews and nieces who looked so much like my own child. I flicked through them, read their names and the dates written on the back of each photo, trying to piece together who belonged to whom. They were strangers and yet there was something familiar about them. I glanced at the next photograph of a middle-aged woman, who I guessed to be Marie. I held her in my hands, touching her face, letting my fingers rest on her. On the first photograph she looked ordinary. We had the same pale-looking skin, features, hair colour. Marie was tall and slim. I pulled out another photograph. On this one, Marie's blonde hair was piled up, and make-up immaculately applied. She looked like she bothered with herself.

I suppose I was always going to be disappointed because, although the image on that photograph was for real, it didn't match my expectation. How could this woman match the imaginary Marie, who had been the fantasy figure of my childhood. Seeing her photo felt like Christmas morning, but after you've opened all your presents.

I had imagined her to be young still, almost frozen in time from when she lost her twins. It was a shock that she had aged – and I was suddenly aware of my own mortality – glimpsing into the reflection of my past, I had peeped into the mirror of my future. In another photograph, I saw a mother, a brother and two sisters in 1970s-style clothes, red hair in pigtails and wearing tank tops, a chopper bike thrown against the wall of their family home, but there was something else I couldn't work out. And then I realised what it was – laid out before me were the pictures of a previous life, one that I could have lived.

Will came in through the front door, but I told him that I couldn't sit around looking at pictures of strangers all day. I was going to paint the upstairs spare room windowsill. I angrily scraped the chair back and I was off, leaving Marie where she was, discarded on the table.

As I stomped up the first few stairs, I turned to look at him. Will had the photographs in his hands, turning them over, putting one behind the other.

'Humph, don't you go saying I look like her,' I said.

'No, I wouldn't dare, love…'

Finding Tommy had been exciting, maybe that had been because he was the first one. It was, perhaps, not such an intimate feeling finding out about your father. Finding your mother was much more of a big deal.

Will, Mum, and I climbed reluctantly back onto yet another emotional fairground ride. The trouble was that even if we weren't enjoying the experience, we knew it wouldn't be ending for some time. Nobody could have prepared us for the conflicting feelings we experienced when faced with a myriad of new family members.

What we were embarking upon on wouldn't just affect Marie and me. Relationships in both our families could be changed. Over the coming months, several families had to rearrange themselves. It wasn't for the fainthearted.

*

I decided I wasn't going to try to make sense of it all now; that was clearly going to take a while. I'd wasted so much time with over-thinking – more than most it seemed. Had I worried more about my roots than the 'average' adopted person? Of course, the average adopted person doesn't exist, but I knew that a displaced sense of self, a longing for identity, is common to many of us.

I sanded down the wooden windowsill, stopping eventually to wipe the dust from my eyes and gaze through the bedroom window's tiny panes. I glanced at the apple tree as a squirrel flung itself down though the top branches, leaping from one to the other. Making the leaves quiver, it weaved its way along the boughs. That squirrel had no worries about parentage. It would be easier to be like him, mindful only of the immediate task, accepting of fate.

I needed to understand that the Marie in the photograph, however lovely, was a stranger to me, not like the mother I'd imagined. She looked like she could be kind – and motherly. The motherly was the startling part. The photographs had shown her cradling her grandchildren, caring for them.

Her daughters had strong-looking features, framed by manes of dark wavy hair. Her son Patrick was photographed wearing a lumber jacket. With shoulder-length, black curly hair falling onto his collar, he looked like everyone's stereotypical image of an Irishman. I couldn't be part of her, couldn't have come from her. They must have found the wrong person. I had imagined her so often, felt connected to her, yet I was left with just an ordinary woman.

Chapter 12

The phone call

More letters arrived.

Dear Dervla,

Thank you for your lovely letter. I understand very much how you must be feeling. I agree with you, that we ought to take things slowly.

Well, Dervla, you wanted to know about the Irish connection. Well, it's a bit of a story. I was born in Ireland, in Limerick City. My mother and father were from Ireland, all my relations are Irish. But, I was adopted and brought up in Yorkshire.

I had a very unhappy childhood, and suffered mental and verbal abuse. I left home at fifteen.

I couldn't wait to get away from them. I met Tommy when I was sixteen. When I was seventeen, and pregnant with you, he took me to Ireland to meet my real parents. It was a traumatic time for me. My parents had stayed married and I had eight sisters and another brother. My father died eighteen months ago. My mother is still alive. So, as the picture unfolds for you, you might understand better why I couldn't keep you. When Tommy walked away from me I had no support from any family. Tommy was my family. At the time, in fact, he was everything to me. When I found myself alone and pregnant I made a decision to marry, not for love, but because I wanted to keep you with me but that didn't work out.

I soon realised that you weren't going to stand any chance of a decent life. I had suffered so much growing up. I wasn't going to hand you to my aunt and uncle. I was afraid that they might put you through what they had done to me.

I thought about everything, even though I was very young. I really was in a desperate situation. Dervla, I'm only telling you this so you will know the truth. I'm so happy that you have had a wonderful childhood, it's all I could have wished for you, and yes, it does help me.

Well, Dervla, about my son Patrick, he is thirty-four and has a daughter. He is a probation officer and lives in the countryside. Carla is thirty-two and she is a civil servant, she works in a social security office. Carla has two children. And Helena! Helena is nearly twenty-nine and manages a restaurant, but she wants to train to be a social worker. She has two children. Helena is an animal lover, like you. She is a very determined person.

About myself, I work as a warden for senior citizens and live on site, I have them knocking on the door regularly. I have always worked in the caring profession. I used to work with autistic children and adults. I have so many siblings, and they are lovely, they are scattered all around England and Ireland. I have a wonderful relationship with my sisters and brother, even though I didn't grow up with them, so good comes out of all the sadness.

The pictures of you and Sasha took my breath away, thank you so much for the photographs. Carla thinks Sasha looks like me. I hope you have found this letter interesting, I do hope it gives you some information about me. I would be delighted for you to phone me. I'm sure you and I will be okay together when we do eventually meet. I'm very easy going and young in my outlook, so I'm told. So bye for now. Hope to hear from you soon.

Lots of love,

Marie

xxxxxx

I was beginning to build a picture of Marie's life. Through her letters, I was able to glimpse into the world she now occupied. I had learned a little about her, her children, and no less importantly, her past. Just before Christmas 2004, I received another one of her letters, with the important closing lines that would enable us to move even further forward.

Here's my number, Dervla. I really would love to speak to you, when you're ready. I can't wait, love Marie. xxx

The only preparation I made before phoning Marie was to collect a steaming mug of tea, an ashtray, and more roll ups. I kept staring at her phone number, written in her tiny handwriting – the sort of handwriting that you'd expect of someone who'd left school at fifteen and had had no more education.

Terrified to hear her voice, but unable to resist, I pressed the numbers on the phone. The connection took a few moments. When she answered it sounded like she'd been running.

'Hello?'

She sounded cross, breathless, a bit overwhelmed.

'Hello Marie, it's Dervla.'

Marie gasped. It sounded like she was crying. Then there was a pause.

'Are you all right, Marie?'

'Yes, yes love. I didn't expect you, I never thought… I never thought I'd hear from you.'

A broad South Yorkshire accent, stilted with emotion, drifted down the line, so unexpectedly different from the imagined Irish voice.

'Is this a bad time?' I didn't know what else to say.

'No love, hang on, let me shut the door…'

Within a few seconds she was back.

'Sorry, love, Vernon doesn't know about you yet,' she whispered conspiratorially into the phone.

'Is Vernon your husband?'

'Well, sort of, although we're not married. It's not that I'm ashamed of you, Dervla, but I haven't found the right time to tell him about you yet.' Her voice brightened. 'Oh, how lovely to hear from you darlin'. I'm made up to hear your voice. I never thought it would happen all those years ago, when I lost my babies.'

'It's lovely to hear your voice, Marie. Do you mind me ringing then?'

'No, sweetheart.' Her words were warm. 'How can I mind? I'm your mother.'

Hearing this made me wince. I felt she had no claim on that title.

'A mother loves her children even if she loses them,' she said, as if she could hear my own thoughts.

There was a pause as I took in the enormity of what she'd just said.

'Thank you.'

'Now, I want to hear about you, Dervla.'

I hadn't been called Dervla since I'd been adopted – at least, only by hospitals and doctors that is. The NHS hadn't got the hang of my new identity either. But Dervla was the name Marie had given me, so I guessed I was going to have to get used to it. Nevertheless, I tried to set her straight.

'Most people call me, Dizzy.'

'Oh… Dizzy, Diz.'

This lasted for exactly thirty seconds, then it was back to Dervla again. It's obviously hard to change the habit of a lifetime.

We talked about my twin, who had died at a few days old, about Tommy and how much she had loved him, still loved him perhaps, about my half-siblings, her job, where she lived, her Irish family. She said how strange it was that she was talking to a grown woman who had once been her baby. She made me cry with laughter, then just cry. She was warm and caring. I got the impression she took care of everybody. Except she hadn't taken care of me.

She talked with such love about her other children, that I knew family was hugely important to her. Naturally or not, I wondered what had I done wrong for her to not want to keep me? She talked about how she would do anything for her children. About how she'd had a terrible time when barely eighteen, with no choice but to have her baby adopted.

The call lasted for three hours. When it was over I couldn't remember a thing about what we talked about. I couldn't even remember what she sounded like. I wasn't sure if my heart was opening up, or closing down for good.

I went to find Will, who was watching *Pearl Harbour* again. He was on the sofa, flanked by the dogs.

'Sorry it took so long, Will,' I said.

He rolled me a cigarette and switched off his film.

'That's all right, love. How did it go?'

His eyes told me he was worried, that he was hoping for positive news.

'She's lovely, I think. Sorry, I can't take it all in, she's obviously not like I expected. I'm sure she feels confused by it all. Actually – it must be awful for her.'

I spilt it all out between more tears. With Will as the best listener, I was able to re-live the conversation, going over it to help me remember, never wanting to ever forget talking to her for the first time.

'And she isn't stupid, she sounds really smart,' I said, getting angry. 'That social worker was cruel and a liar in what she said about Marie in that birth file. My God, Marie was little more than a child when all this happened to her.'

A child who was now claiming her right to be my mother. But I already had one, a consistent mother who had been able to stand by me – and who I didn't want to hurt. She'd said it was fine, of course, but that was earlier, when the idea of finding Marie was abstract. Now it was feeling very real. I'd been driven by my need to find out, but nothing had prepared me for my conflicting emotions, for how easily people could get hurt, for what it might mean to have a whole new set of people in our lives.

My feelings of uncertainty before were nothing to the anxieties I was experiencing now. And most of them, at this stage, were around my adoptive mother.

I went back to Paula and we sat in her kitchen again. How things had changed since we had sat at the same table reading the birth file.

'I don't have to carry on with this – not if it's hurting you, Mum.'

'I'm fine; I think it will help you. Everyone needs to know where they come from.'

She reached her hand across the table, squeezing my hand in hers.

'I want you to know, it doesn't hurt me. I have to be honest though, I'm worried about you going to meet Marie on your own. I would come with you, but I don't think it would be appropriate. How about Will?'

'He's always so busy,' I replied.

'Sugar? Sugar would come with you.'

'I'll be okay, Mum', I said.

Later she wrote me a letter.

CHAPTER 13

WORDS FROM MY ADOPTIVE MUM TO ME

I believe in fate. I think you are in control of most of your life, but I believe something occasionally occurs over which you have no control and it changes the path of your life forever.

I had lost two babies. I couldn't have any more, so ten years after Ellis was born we decided to adopt. The process was long and tedious, but we were accepted and, eventually, we had a letter to say a baby was available. We signed the acceptance letter and walked to the post box to send it. I was carrying the envelope, but just as I was about to put it in the post box, something made me hesitate.

'I can't do it,' I said. 'Supposing I have her home and can't love her, it would be terrible for both of us.' With that, my husband – and your father, Terry – took the letter out of my hand and popped it in the box.

In the beginning we could only visit you once a week for an hour, and we had to stay in the foster home. I was so afraid you would forget us that I started wearing the same perfume every time in the hope it would remind you of me. It's strange, because you have always had a keen sense of smell, and are emotionally affected by certain ones.

One day the powers that be said we could take you out for the afternoon. It had been snowing and the trees were heavy with snow and icicles. We drove out into the country, stopped the car, wrapped you in a blanket and carried you out under the trees. You were seven months and you looked up in wonder at the sun shining on the snow-covered branches. We shook the tree gently and the first snow came down and sprinkled your face. You loved it, and I saw you laugh for the first time.

When you finally came home, it was difficult for a couple of weeks, and you needed constant cuddling. Sometimes, when you wouldn't settle, my mum would take you and walk the room singing "O God, our help in ages past". You knew then who was in charge.

Once you entered our lives, we knew you were as much a part of us as our own son. For a long time I would put you to bed, kiss you, tell you stories, but I could never go back into the bedroom to check if you were asleep. The sight of your pale, quiet face with closed eyes, filled me with memories. Even now, after all these years, I find something unsettling in a silent baby.

You brought joy into our lives and still do, but I often think of your birth mum. When she contacted you, Dizzy, I think you were afraid it would hurt me, but it never did. The bond between us is too great. It has been established through years of good and bad experiences, and if your love has survived that, nothing will diminish it.

*

So, I kept checking with Mum, that she was all right, and the Friday night phone calls continued with Marie. It became a kind of pattern. Paula was the real-life, here and now mother; Marie was the might-have-been, somewhere-else mother, a voice on the telephone line.

I kept myself supplied with tea and cigarettes, Will kept himself supplied with old movies. Sasha could keep herself busy rescuing animals. We could carry on like that; there was nothing to get alarmed about – until the Friday when Marie said; 'I want to see you, Dervla. When can you come?'

Chapter 14

Meeting Marie

So there I was, suitcase by my side, on that train, pulling up at Sheffield station. I remember thinking that, of all the places we could have chosen, this certainly wasn't the most beguiling. My stomach lurched as the train ground to a halt alongside the platform. This journey had taken five hours and four decades.

I was in the last carriage. Outside there were people waiting, but they were all further up ahead, no-one was looking my way. I joined the queue in the aisle to get off the train, hastily making escape plans. I could wrap my scarf round my head, rush to the exit, cross over to the downline platform. Go home.

But of course I knew it was far too late. I was already completely entangled. The realisation released a metallic taste into my mouth, one I hadn't tasted since pregnancy.

As soon as the train door was opened, passengers rushed to alight. A guard strode down the platform, slamming doors. As I heaved my suitcase, trailing at the back of the crowds of commuters, my legs felt like they might give way. I leaned against a concrete pillar, trying to steady myself, and stared up the platform. It was then I caught the first glimpse of my two half-sisters.

I knew them immediately, their faces made familiar by their photographs. But the black-and-white Polaroids hadn't shown me how pretty their eyes were – almond-shaped and green.

We made our way through the crowds, pushing our way towards each other.

'Dizzy, love, oh God, you're here!' Carla said, eyes smiling, but filling with tears. 'I've been waiting all my life for you. Give us a hug.'

We must have looked a peculiar sight.

'Mum's going demented – your train was so late! We'd better get a move on,' said Helena. She and Carla rushed me to the escalator. Reaching the top, I saw her.

Catching sight of us, she raised her arm in the air, 'Dervla!'

She gained speed as she approached me – almost running – hurrying across the railway station, oblivious of other passengers. In my head, I had a picture of my birth mother that was formed when I was very young. Over the years, it had been embellished by imagination until she had become a fantasy figure, created out of my longing for knowledge. My mind's image was, of course, nothing like this character who was heading ever faster towards me. She was no red-headed, green-eyed Riverdancer with a soft Wexford accent, that was for sure. In reality, her appearance was more like Bet Lynch, about to serve behind the bar of the Rovers Return. Her well-groomed appearance, although glamorous, somehow struck me as harsh. She wore pointy-toed, knee-length boots that wouldn't suit my West Country feet.

And then she was there. The wait was over. Marie and I finally met face to face at Sheffield train station.

Her long black leather coat engulfed me, as the scary creature that was my birth mother embraced me – finally, after all these years. And yet whatever I felt, surely this was worse for her. I'd thought I was hardened. I'd kept telling myself that any separation anxiety had vanished long ago, that I was just here to tell her she had nothing to worry about – that it wouldn't mean that much to me.

I was surprised how shocked I was by the reality of her. Marie's perfume wasn't cheap, but it was overpowering. It masked her true smell, a smell I didn't remember, one that had been taken away from me. Instead, I had learned to recognise the scent of another mother, one who was steady and protective, and I had learned to love her perfume most in the world.

But Marie and I clung to each other as if we would never have to let go again. Still holding onto me, she dragged me off to see the rest of her family who'd been standing patiently outside a take-away coffee booth at the entrance to the station. They had formed a line, waiting to be introduced like wedding guests ready to greet a bride and groom before the reception. In the line-up was a mix of dark hair, auburn hair, pale skin and big eyes. Despite the differences in colouring, though, to me they all looked the same. A handsome bunch of strangers – but among them all, I thought, Carla was the real beauty.

The mood changed as our initial nervousness took its leave. For a moment, at least, meeting them felt surprisingly normal. The first awkward silences didn't bother me, I was glad of the pauses in conversation, because there was so much to take in.

There were moments when we didn't know what to do. After all, there's no manual. Eventually, the pauses became fewer as this new family did what they knew best – they all started talking at once. It soon became apparent that these strangers were not a quiet bunch. Marie filled any long lapses in conversation by turning towards me and smiling, soaking me in. She'd let go of me now, but she was affectionate, she kept reaching out and touching me as if to make sure I was real. This was her day.

She wore heavy make-up. Dark long lashes set off her green eyes, feline, translucent, taking me in – and as familiar as my mirror image. Her blonde hair was piled up in a loose bun. Either side of her face, wispy bits of hair had been gently teased out and curled so symmetrically that it couldn't have been an accident. Her lipstick ran very slightly over the top of her Cupid's bow, framing a mouth shaped like a porcelain doll's. Her alabaster complexion was almost hidden under a layer of foundation, though the make-up could not disguise her true Celtic skin.

She covered over any angst she might have been feeling and began moving us all along to where her car was parked. I was bundled into the back, along with my two half-sisters. The new family, it seemed, had kidnapped me.

I sat there, staring at Marie's head and shoulders in the front. At last, here she was, solid and very much alive. Next to her, driving, was a bemused-looking man called Vernon, who had been unaware until recently that his partner of over twenty years had a secret. Neither Marie, nor the rest of her family had ever mentioned her past to him. He'd had no clue about what had happened to her all those years ago. Keeping such a big secret seemed odd, but I realised there was so much I didn't know about Marie – and who was I to judge her?

At no time did she make me feel anything but welcome. Although it was peculiar, I did feel as if I could be part of this family. At the same time, though, it was as if I'd met these people on a holiday. As if we'd all had a great fortnight, back in 1968, despite the teenage pregnancy and the abandonment, so I'd just gone back to stay for a couple of days so we could all relive the experience.

Elvis Presley's "Always On My Mind" was playing in the car. I was cynical. Had it been planned? Afterwards, whenever I visited Marie, Elvis was always playing in the background of our lives. At that moment, though, instead of bringing us closer, hearing him had the same effect as the last song played at a teenage disco when the music and the magic is over, and you come face to face in the harsh lights. And however caring and however lovely she was, she wasn't as I'd imagined her – it was unrealistic to think that she would have been. Neither could I respond to her in the way she had reacted to me. What I was feeling wasn't affection – it was more like aversion. Registering this, I felt at fault; culpable in that

I might have let my aversion show. Guilty that I'd already hurt her; convicted of not being good enough.

*

Marie's house was immaculately clean. At least, I assumed the bungalow was Marie's; there was no time to ask about such inconsequential information. More relatives were presented. I'd been doing all right until I saw the children; little dots with huge eyelashes, framing emerald eyes that searched our faces in puzzlement. All so similar looking to my own child that I had to look away as they were introduced.

'This is Auntie Dervla, who's been missing,' Marie said. For this family had always viewed me in this way. I soon became aware that I'd always been discussed with Marie's children – spoken of as part of the family, not seen as a shameful secret. It was just Vernon who had never been told.

I'd been getting on, having a marvellous life of course, unaware of them as real people, thinking of them as mysterious story book characters, who might or might not one day appear in the flesh. Having discovered that grave, and having believed Marie to be dead, made it even more difficult to reconcile the past with the present.

Chapter 15

Just an Ordinary Afternoon

Later, once the relatives had been dispatched, Vernon drove Marie and me to the nearest pub.

Finally, we could be on our own.

Our recent letters and phone calls had gone some way to lessen the awkwardness, but Marie still felt like a stranger. I couldn't quite comprehend that she had given birth to me. I felt as if everything had happened to someone else, as if I was standing in for them. But I couldn't stop looking at her face. Despite our different styles, we were strikingly similar, so there was definitely no mix up on the part of social services.

Still unable to get over seeing her in the flesh, I made my excuses and went to the bathroom. I was dawdling in the cubicle, mopping up tears with bits of loo-roll, trying to compose myself, when I heard her outside the toilet door.

'Are you all right, love? You've been ages. Thought you'd changed your mind and gone back to Bristol. You're not ashamed of me, are you?'

'No! Don't be daft, Marie,' I replied, 'I'm not here to judge you.'

We tucked ourselves into a little corner of the pub, and sat next to each other. I sat sideways on the chair to watch her. The afternoon that followed was filled with Marie's grief and regret, most of which was probably easier to say as it was fuelled by Chardonnay. She seemed driven by a desperate need to explain her actions of so many years ago. We covered nine months and thirty-six years in three hours. But during that time, I discovered that Marie was funny, open and honest. As the afternoon and the wine took effect, I began to warm to her.

Perhaps her recounting of events went some way towards helping me understand the predicament she had found herself in. Pregnant with twins in 1967, an Irish Catholic and homeless. She had little option but to give up her baby, a double grief as her other twin baby girl died at a few days old. Marie had lost both of us.

I had been raised to think the best of her, with only sympathy and understanding for the situation she faced. So, I pulled myself together to go through the motions of what I'd been taught. I tried desperately to take Marie's guilt away – kept telling her it wasn't her fault, and that it was all right now. Nevertheless, there were times when empathy failed.

Marie was the bigger hearted of us. Her tragic life events hadn't made her bitter. In fact, she had grown from them to be a compassionate and caring woman.

'I didn't have any choice but to give you up. Tommy left me pregnant a week before our wedding,' said Marie.

'You were going to get married?'

'We loved each other so much. We were engaged, had been for eighteen months. We'd been to Ireland and everything to ask permission from my father and the priest to get married over there. They both said no. It made me so angry. I felt my father had no right to say no to me. When Tommy and I returned, we arranged for the wedding to be back here in England. Finally, my father sent a permission letter. Well, my mother must have got hold of him. I expect she explained that if I didn't get married my life would be over. That was what it was like back then. But shortly after Tommy and I got back to England,' she continued, 'he went back to the barracks, while I stayed with his mother. We were meant to be getting married, but only a few days before the wedding he sent a letter, breaking it off. He said he was being posted to South East Asia, so his mother kicked me out. I ended up homeless.'

'Oh Marie,' I said, and from that moment the sympathy I felt for her was real.

'A few months later,' she went on, 'I married a man who was known to the family. He'd always fancied me,' Marie paused to recollect the events that led to my adoption. 'I thought I'd be able to keep you if I did all the right things. But as the pregnancy wore on, it became apparent that he didn't want you. I worked night-shifts in a factory to try to save up some money, but it was useless really. It wasn't 'till I'd actually given birth to you that the midwife said there was another baby in there. There were no scans in those days. You only weighed three and a half pounds each, you were little scraps of things. You had to go into incubators, so they took you off.'

'Did you get to hold us?'

'Yes, of course, every day, but I didn't feed you. Your twin died at three days old, and after ten days I left hospital without either of you. It broke my heart. I never went to the funeral, they wouldn't let me out of the hospital. Mothers stayed in for a week or more back then.' She paused again. 'At that time, Tommy was abroad, so he didn't even know you'd been born or what had happened to your twin. We weren't able to bury our own child.'

How tragic it was that her whole life had been marred at the age of seventeen when she found herself pregnant. She had endured an enormous amount of sadness – too much for one person.

'I had a breakdown,' she said. 'It were several years back, but I'm all right now, love. Having you sitting here in front of me, seeing my child. I never thought this would happen.'

Guilt set in. Obviously, I hadn't chosen any of this to happen, but since my arrival into this world, Marie's life had been set to be a disaster. I wondered if we were both still defined by the events that happened such a long time ago, the consequences of which had been so far reaching.

'I feel so bad that all those things made you ill,' I said.

'It's not your fault. Things were different back then, Dervla. People didn't go to counselling in my day. They sent me to hospital in the end, years later. Poor Vernon, he's such a kind man. And poor Carla! She's such a worrier – she'd only just had her first child at that time.'

'Did they keep you there for a long time?'

'Yes, a fair time, till they made me better.'

'What happened?' I asked. 'What happened when Tommy left?'

'When you were well enough to leave the hospital, I put you in a private foster home. I visited you all the time. Then social services stepped in, trying to persuade me to let you go. You were my baby, no one else's, but they seemed to forget that. They kept bringing these papers for me to sign, giving my permission. I was all over the place, I was only just eighteen. I couldn't take you back to my house as my husband didn't want you, so...' She broke off mid-sentence and looked down at the table.

I lit a cigarette. It was exhausting, trying to make sense of it all; trying to catch up on decades of information in one afternoon. But Marie had much more to tell me.

'I couldn't take you back to my own foster parents to live. My foster mum offered, but my foster father was a bastard. I wouldn't have let him get his hands on you. He was a cruel man. In the end, the social worker put so much pressure on, telling me you'd have a good life somewhere else, a life I couldn't offer you, that in the end I believed it. I did it for your own good, but not for mine. I never wanted you to go away from me, Dervla, I wanted you with me. I tried everything to keep you.' She reached out and stroked my hand. 'I used to get you from the foster carer all the time, take you out for a few hours. One day I had to take you to the social worker so she could see how I was trying to care for you. She wanted to get her hands on you. She was a bitch to me, pressing me to sign all these forms, telling me it was the right thing to do. I was busy trying to feed you, but you were fractious that day. It wasn't anything I'd done, but she said to me "She doesn't know you". I had so little control over my life, she tried to take that last thing away from me – the fact that you and I had a bond.'

That afternoon, we consumed a whole bottle of wine, which wasn't a wise thing to do, because alcohol, Marie told me, gave her a migraine. This particular session resulted in Vernon getting the car out again to come and collect us. He pulled up outside the pub and wound down the window.

'Oh, crap, look at the state of her,' he said. 'She'll have to lie in a darkened room when we get back. It can take up to three days to shift one of her headaches.'

I sat on Marie's large white sofa, which was so big my legs wouldn't reach the floor. I was tucked up waiting patiently for my mum. Although I was thirty-six, I felt about ten years old, but with the attitude of a teenager. The room felt hot, a gas fire hummed out its warmth. I looked around; the room was cream, minimalistic. Marie clearly didn't like clutter. The only ornament was a silver and white Art Deco figurine, carefully placed, which sat alone on the mantelpiece shelf looking down on us.

Vernon and I sat next to each other, facing the biggest television screen on earth. That day, I watched TV for the first time in years. I normally only listened to the radio as I agree with the subliminal advertising theory. That couldn't possibly be happening to Radio 4 listeners! I glanced at my watch. It was seven o'clock. I was going to miss *The Archers*.

When Marie surfaced, she looked washed out; her face, without the foundation, was pale. Despite how she must be feeling, she leapt up and started bustling about in the kitchen, clanking pots, rummaging in the fridge.

'What do you want for tea, Dervla?' she asked. 'What would you like, love? I can make you anything.'

I refused her offer of dinner. I didn't want to eat her food – I didn't want her to give me anything. It was too late to fix things with a meal. After all the years of wondering, there was too much to digest. What I did know, though, was that I didn't want meat and two veg on a tray in front of the telly.

CHAPTER 16

THE JEREMY KYLE EXPERIENCE

I stepped out of Marie's bungalow into the damp January streets. I'd promised her I wouldn't be long, wouldn't wander far, but ended up going miles down the road to get a signal –

'What are they like, Diz?' Will asked.

'Kind, they're really kind, Will.'

He'd been waiting all day to hear this news. I imagined him in our home, surrounded by trees rather than the rows of grey terraced and prefabricated houses I was now facing. I found the tiny gardens and yards depressing; there was no greenery, no space to be yourself. As much as anything else, this day had been a culture shock.

'And what's it like there?' he asked.

'You'd hate it up here, you don't like the city at the best of times,' I said.

'But you're okay?'

'I wish I were home with you,' I told him.

I walked back up the street. Darkness had fallen and the windows in Marie's house were lit by lamps; it looked warm and cosy in there, but it wasn't home.

Once I was back inside the bungalow, Marie greeted me like a special guest. I was fussed over, worried about. It seemed bizarre to be here, in Marie's actual house – the events that followed that evening were no less surreal. Carla and Helena came over and we went for a drink at a pub that looked like The Rovers Return. They said we could have gone up social club with Vernon but, as Marie still wasn't feeling well, the two women who called themselves my sisters, accompanied me for the evening.

By midnight, Carla, Helena and I were pissed and in a taxi, telling our whole sorry tale to the driver. He said we ought to be appearing on the *Jeremy Kyle Show*. In fact, he seemed so genuinely pleased about our story that he switched off his meter. At one point, he pulled over to the side of the road and stopped the engine, flicked on the inside light of the car, and turned around so he could scrutinise our faces for any family resemblances. All the while we entertained him with tales of teenage pregnancy, abandonment, private detectives and a reunion of which he was now a part.

'I'm not going to charge you your fare,' he said. 'That's made my night to hear your story.' People "up north" were "right friendly", I thought – it was definite.

I'd already decided that it would be a bit much to stay at Marie's house, so I was booked into a commercial-scale hotel; the sort of thing you find on every motorway services, where the beds smell of dead people. Inside my room, my half-sisters and I consumed Irish Cream until four in the morning. They recounted tales and recalled the visits to stay with their Irish grandmother when they were young.

Putting on their best Irish accents for my benefit, they impersonated her with enthusiasm. 'The ghosts, Dervla, the ghosts! Get under the bed or the devil will come for you.' And the three of us leapt under the duvet, pulling the covers up to our eyes, screeching.

In Carla and Helena, I had found two delightful new friends that I was strangely acquainted with. We shared so many family resemblances. It wasn't long before we had our socks off so we could compare our feet and our three similar sets of unattractive chubby toes. The family trait of the webbed toe was discussed, and we all peered at my foot in mock horror. How did they both manage to squeeze their flat feet into high heels? I glanced furtively at my sensible Doc Marten boots cast aside in the corner of the room. My sisters were open and welcoming. This, as I later learned was true of Marie and all her children, but back then these people were new to me. I was grateful for Carla and Helena's generosity. It swept away the tensions of the day.

I found it easier being with them than Marie. Perhaps it was because there weren't too many years' difference between us and our children were a similar age. All half-siblings together, all born to the same mother, but with a dampening down of the genes, except, I thought, my life had been like one of Vernon's TV programmes, *Lucky Escape to the Country*.

My new-found family had decided for me that I would be lonely in a strange hotel, so Helena had been selected to stay the night with me, and Carla was bundled home in a taxi. Helena and I giggled at the thought that it might be that same driver that we'd met earlier, or the one who had helped Carla break in through her bathroom window recently, after she'd forgotten her key. He'd seen quite a lot of her as she'd climbed through the small opening wearing a short skirt and tiny pants. In fact, the taxi drivers of Sheffield already knew far too much about us.

Helena and I finished off the last of the Irish Cream, but the tone of our conversation became sombre as we got ready for bed. How odd would it be, sharing a double bed with a stranger? Not only that, this stranger was a relative – even more alarmingly, she was my half-sister.

But Helena didn't seem a bit fazed about the sleeping arrangements. As she got ready for bed, she told me of the day a few months before, when she and Carla had accompanied Marie to meet my birth father Tommy.

'I thought I was going to harm him… being there with Mum, seeing her reaction to him. I couldn't believe his nerve.' Helena pulled off her shoes. She disappeared into the bathroom, continuing to shout the conversation through the half-open door. 'Mum was so shocked – she hadn't known she was going to meet him. Carla had a phone call, from this woman, Irene. She said she knew Tommy and asked if Carla would meet her. She said that she had some information about you.'

I heard water filling the sink next door. After a few minutes of her splashing and clattering, it gurgled away as the plug was pulled. The top half of Helena reappeared round the door frame, still holding her toothbrush.

'It was so strange. Carla took me and Mum with her, obviously, because we thought something was up. We went to meet this lady, Irene, but Tommy was waiting.'

'I think he wants to try to put things right, he was very young when it all happened,' I said.

She came out of the bathroom, now waving the toothbrush, pointing it accusingly as she tried to get her message across. She paused between words to scrub dramatically at her teeth.

'Yes, but my poor mum. Christ! This is all Tommy's fault. After all, it's him that facilitated this, what with the private detective and social services!'

'I do think he's truly sorry, and Marie seems relieved to have the chance to explain,' I said. Helena grinned at me. 'She is, of course she is, love.' Her voice softened. 'It's so much better for her, now you're known to her.'

She flung her toothbrush onto the dressing table, then climbed into bed.

'But,' she continued, 'he was the one that made her pregnant. The prat left her for thirty-six years, then hired a private detective and found you. I'm sorry for giving him a hard time. But he really pisses me off.'

She was feisty and outspoken – but who was I to judge?

There was a lot to think about in the three hours of dream time that followed, before another day abruptly started, and we found ourselves on our way back to Marie's – preparing to say goodbye again.

*

It was early when Helena and I entered the bungalow the next morning and I was shocked to hear from Vernon that Marie had already been cleaning for hours. Marie, however, was oblivious to Vernon's concerns. She was in what appeared to be her favourite position, hovering near to her Dyson, ready to plug in and vacuum.

'I've stripped the beds, love, cleaned the windows and sorted out three wardrobes,' she said. She moved further up her kitchen, dishcloth in hand. Vernon shot me a look.

'She's obsessive about cleaning. Her nickname's Marie Dishcloth,' he said.

'Take no notice of him, Dervla,' Marie said, turning her back on Vernon. 'I cleaned out the wardrobes because I was searching for something. I found you this – knew I'd put it somewhere safe.'

Marie held out her hand and signalled for me to take the shiny red box.

I opened its lid. There, nestled inside the tissue paper, was an enormous silver crucifix. Its thin chain was folded back, as if it had fallen to lie peacefully by the side of the cross.

'Oh, it's beautiful! Thank you.'

'I got that for you. I know how you like Irish things. I've missed every one of your birthdays and Christmases. I've never had the chance to buy you anything before,' she said.

I put my hand up to my neck to touch the tiny Celtic cross that my mum Paula had bought for me, the one I always wore.

'It's lovely. Thank you,' I said again.

I placed the new Marie cross round my neck and held up my

hair whilst she fastened the clasp for me. She turned me around to have a look, holding onto my shoulders, taking a step back.

'You look beautiful in that. You're a good looking girl – all my daughters are lovely.' She smiled, pleased that her purchase was correct.

Unfortunately, the cross was so heavy I could hardly stand up straight. I staggered over to the sofa, sitting down quickly next to Helena, with the crucifix threatening to impale me. It felt ridiculous to be wearing two crosses, but I couldn't bring myself to take off the cross from Mum – I wasn't trying to impersonate Madonna.

'I made you some breakfast, Dervla. It's keeping warm in the oven.' Marie disappeared into the kitchen and Vernon grinned over at me from his chair by the telly.

'No good arguing with her, she's been up for hours getting you your breakfast,' he said.

A plate of scrambled eggs, made for me by my mother, what could be simpler? And yet… I was about to attempt to eat the scrambled egg when Carla staggered in through the back door, her two children trailing behind.

'You can just stop with the keeping on at me, Keiron, my back's killin' me. I drank so much last night I think I've permanently damaged me kidneys so I can't play football. NO! Go and ask Grandad Vernon.'

'How are you, Carla?' I asked.

'Oh Jesus,' she groaned, 'I'm crap, love, thanks.'

Before we even left Marie's house to make for the train station, they'd managed to lose one of the grandchildren – Carla's child Jed, who was just eighteen months old. Carla leapt into action. Abandoning her previous lethargic state, lying face-down on the sofa rubbing her back, she was up and out the door as soon as the cry went up that Jed was missing. The entire family became hysterical. They rushed back and forth in a long line past the house, looking like they were about to start the conga. On their third fly past I noticed some neighbours had also joined the line to help. Raised voices and talk of calling the police floated through the window. I longed to be back on the tiny farm where there was peace and quiet, where there were people I knew how to handle. Home suddenly seemed even further away.

I crept into the bedroom to find Jed hiding beside the bed, playing with his toy cars. The tiny red and blue vehicles were laid out in a line. He was concentrating hard, getting them into exactly the right positions. I stole a hug from his solid little body, and kissed the black hair at the nape of his neck, just at the place where the curls touched his skin. Then I gave the game away.

At the train station, Marie was all over me, reaching out to embrace me. She took my face in her hands, planted a kiss on my lips. That, I suppose, is a mother's prerogative. I was now covered in lipstick, like a child. I half expected her to moisten a hanky to wipe the corners of my mouth, like mums do. But this mum hadn't had the chance before, and she didn't have permission now.

'When you next visit... I'm not nagging, I know you're busy... I want to take some time off work, see you properly and for longer. How long do you think you'll be able to stay for? The whole weekend? Could that Will of yours look after Sasha again, or could they come too?'

'I'm not sure.'

I was under no illusion that I could have a quick look at Marie then just disappear, I was already entangled. There was so much to know about these new people who had been catapulted into my life. Other meetings had already been arranged. Apparently, most of Ireland was set to arrive on our doorstep over the coming months. I was going to have to go along with it all. How cruel it would be to fade into the future now – I couldn't do it.

On the train home, as soon as Marie's waving hand was out of sight, and when I had caught the last of the blown kisses, I had a longing to phone my mum, Paula. I waited until we were well out of Sheffield; I needed to leave the past behind me, to let the last twenty-four hours settle.

'Mum.'

'Dizzy? My darling, are you okay?'

'Thank God you're there. Thank you for all that you've done.'

What I said came from the heart; my mum had done the hard work. And now I knew she'd be impatient to hear how everything had gone. It said much about her that she'd given her blessing to the meeting with Marie in the first place. She was just pleased that I'd been given the chance to see where I'd come from. She'd been unselfish – had remained unflinching in her support. Even though this was undoubtedly hard for her, she never let it show. Throughout our lives, she'd always done anything she could to help Ellis and me. Over the past few weeks, both my mum and Will's mum had phoned frequently for updates on how my big adventure was progressing.

In six short months I had acquired an entire new family. I had managed to meet my birth father, Tommy, discovered that my birth mother, Marie, was alive, and had also met my half-siblings. And yet, this journey was only just beginning. Now my family at home had a whole new collection of people to get used to. It had been arranged that my mum would meet Marie in a few months time. At that moment, speaking to her on the phone, I decided that mothers would go through anything when it came to their children. Even if they didn't know them.

Chapter 17

Tommy and the Quad Convoy

As I got to know more about Tommy, it became clear that he was someone who was always having adventures. On his next one, he told me, he and a friend were to ride their quad bikes to Cornwall, each with a passenger, starting from his home near Hawes in Yorkshire. Tommy was going to take along a disabled friend, Peter. As Peter had a prosthetic leg, Tommy had adapted the quad to make it as comfortable as possible for him to manage the trip riding pillion.

We knew they would be passing near to our house on the way, so Will and I weren't surprised when we received a telephone call from Tommy one evening. But what we were surprised about was another member of the party.

'Can we pop in, chuck? I'd like you to meet my son.'

'Simon or Martin?' I asked.

'No, Dizzy. There's another one – Nick. He was born before you...'

I didn't reply. After a long and awkward pause, Tommy carried on as if he'd read my thoughts.

'I didn't tell you about him before. You see we were only reunited a couple of years ago.'

Our genetic pool was obviously far reaching.

'We could pop in tomorrow evening?'

*

But Sasha and I were to meet the quad convoy earlier than planned. We were returning from the annual school photo session with Merlin in tow. As Sasha didn't have any human siblings, he'd gone down to the school to be photographed too. It was, after all, perfectly normal for our family to consider a dog to be as much a member of the family as any human. Even though the headmistress had given Merlin a withering look and muttered something unfriendly about me insisting on breaching the school's Health and Safety policy, she'd let him in.

Merlin had had a doubly successful day. Firstly, he managed to stand still while Sasha gave an afternoon assembly to her class mates about rescue greyhounds. I was slightly surprised at his new, calm approach. I sat in the corner of the school hall, unable to relax in case he had a relapse, and watched him showing off for all of the children and behaving impeccably. I hadn't put him down as a dog that liked an audience, but given his recent dramas it shouldn't have been such a surprise.

Secondly, he posed for the camera like an old pro while the school photographer squeaked a toy "to get the greyhound's ears up". The toy was the alarming part; it would have challenged the canine composure of most dogs. But there was no need to be on edge: the village school children were made up to meet Merlin, and he revelled in all the fuss, graciously allowing himself to be patted by forty tiny hands.

While Merlin was off all medication, I was still in need of some – the last few months of interaction with my new family had left me decidedly shaky. So, initially, I thought that a new herbal range at Boots that promised a new calm you was a bit of a find. A display board showed pictures of serene-looking people standing in fields of poppies, with the sun shining. I obediently took these new wonder tablets daily after the discovery of my birth family, with no calming affect that Will or I had noticed.

So, an accidental early meeting in a lay-by with Tommy was the last thing I needed. It was only as a hasty chat, because as soon as Merlin spotted the bike he started licking our car window in an attempt to break free, but in the short time we had, Tommy disclosed that Peter wouldn't be coming over to our house as planned with the rest of them. Earlier that day, he had lost his prosthetic leg somewhere in Somerset. It had fallen off the quad bike and run away.

I cornered Tommy when we were out of earshot of the others.

'It would have been good to know there was another sibling. It was a shock you telling us only yesterday, then just turning up with him,' I said.

Tommy met my gaze.

'Why do you keep holding back information?' I asked.

'Well,' Tommy replied, 'I keep thinking it must be a bit much for you all.'

'It's a bit much when you turn up with a half-brother out of the blue,' I told him. 'Look, I'll see you later – seven o'clock. You've got the postcode. Don't be late!'

I drove Sasha and the window-licking Merlin home, stomped into the house and rang my mother.

'You wouldn't fancy fish and chips would you, Mum? It's just that Tommy's arriving here tonight and I thought it would be a good chance for you to meet him.'

'Yes, all right – we'll come over. We've had tea, but Al can always manage more, though I can't tolerate fried food, as you know. Is everything okay, Diz?'

'Um, well, Tommy's coming here, but not just him, he's

bringing one of his mates and another half-brother that I didn't know about called Nick. Would you like to meet them, Mum?'

'You know I would. I've always wondered whether there were more.'

So, that evening poor Peter was left in a hotel room, while Tommy, plus mystery half-brother Nick, made their way to our house for fish and chips.

Nick was the spit of Tommy, and also very affable. He had been born eighteen months before me, but hadn't been reunited with Tommy until a couple of years ago. Even so, they seemed to have developed a great friendship, and saw each other often. I started to wonder if there could in fact be even more Tommy offspring roaming the country, seeking out fun. According to Tommy, all his children seemed to like taking off and having adventures.

Mum's silver car arrived promptly, creeping almost silently down the driveway, without a fuss. My mum and my step-dad, Al, made it look like they'd just popped in. Tommy was sitting on the seat in our front garden. He made the first move, jumping to his feet immediately and extending a hand. But my mum did all the talking, she chattered on and on and soon she overwhelmed him.

'I'll just take these bags into the kitchen, Tommy – see you in a minute,' she said. 'You chat to Tommy, Al,' she instructed my step-dad. Then she shot me "The Look". This was my cue.

She made her way swiftly into the house, with me obediently following. She didn't waste much time before she had me cornered in the kitchen. Warming her hands by laying them across the lids of the Rayburn, she started muttering in a stage whisper. With exaggerated lip movements, she made it known to me that she was less than impressed with the treatment and abandonment of Peter.

'What's Tommy done with him? Poor man. I think it's terrible.'

'I think Peter wanted to wait at the hotel. He's tired, Mum. And anyway, it's none of our business.'

'How can they have lost his leg? It's not very caring,' she went on.

'I don't know,' I said. 'Perhaps they didn't strap it on properly.'

'Haven't they got a spare?'

'Mum, how many people do you know who carry a spare leg?'

'I don't know about that, but I've never met anyone like Tommy, that's for sure. I don't know what to make of it all, and who's that man with him again?'

'My half-brother Nick, apparently. He was born before me. Tommy didn't bring him up either, they were only reunited a couple of years ago.'

'Well, I can see that he's the spitting image of his dad, but I can't say he looks anything like you. And who was his mother, I wonder?'

She edged closer to me, still resting her elbows on the Rayburn lids, her back against its cosy, reassuring presence. She whispered more loudly than was wise when you're trying not to be overheard by people in the garden.

'How many children do you think Tommy has?'

'Mother, please!'

Mum bit her bottom lip. She didn't say any more. We sat in the garden that evening eating our chips, all chatting away – all except Mum who was obviously distracted – probably worried about the enigma that was Peter. She kept looking at her watch and sighing. When Tommy finally said they should get back to the hotel, she looked visibly relieved. I knew she was hiding her true feelings. I knew, too, that she wouldn't be able to contain her concern for much longer. One of her advice notes was sure to arrive over the next few days – she wouldn't be able to stop herself.

I stood with her at the gate, waving everyone away. The noise of the quad engines got quieter and quieter as they disappeared down the hill and out of view. We stood there until we could no longer hear them. Then we stood some more, just in case they should come back.

'It's none of my business, but...'

'Not now, Mum.'

'Sorry, it's just…'

'No,' I said, holding up my hand. 'I'm going in now. I need a cigarette, and a glass of wine, a large glass that has a cork in the top.'

But I knew that we hadn't heard the last of this.

Early the next morning, just when I thought it was safe to carry on with my less-than-normal life, I was woken up by Merlin going ballistic. The quad convoy was back again and roaring down the drive; this time, Peter was in tow.

'Just dropping in to have a cuppa and bid farewell,' Tommy reassured me.

'Yes, right, tea then…'

'We'll have it outside, if that's all right,' said Tommy. 'It's exhausting for Peter to have to keep being moved on and off the bike.'

I put the kettle on and fussed about in the kitchen, setting out mugs, milk and sugar on a tray and tried to pacify Merlin with bone-shaped treats to distract him from glaring out of the window and growling.

It was difficult to get through the front door with all the tea things, while keeping Merlin back. My commands for him to stay were clearly in a language that was foreign to him.

'Stay!'

Merlin pushed his long nose through the gap between my leg and the door frame. He wiggled it to open the gap further and reached out his front leg to scratch the tiny space wider.

'STAY!'

I rushed up the garden path towards the quad bikers, managing to spill most of the tea. The milk splashed over into the sugar bowl.

'Have you got a spoon please, chuck?' Tommy asked.

So I went back into the house to fetch him a spoon, leaving Peter with his half mug of tea. Although pale, he looked chipper, reposing on the bike in the early morning sunshine. I was glad to see he was properly strapped onto the quad. I would report this good news to my mother later – she was going to be delighted to hear that he still had the one good leg.

'How many miles have we got to cover today?' asked Nick.

'More than we'll manage,' said Tommy, folding up the map. 'We ought to be getting on our way. Next stop is Bodmin for brunch.'

Tommy climbed onto the quad. I bent down to kiss his cheek, feeling sad all over again that he was leaving once more.

'Remember, whatever else you do, have fun, Dizzy,' Tommy yelled above the noise of the revving bikes. He rammed on his crash helmet, fastened the strap and nodded to the others.

Will came out from the forge to fold his arms across his chest in a gesture of bike appreciation that only the initiated could understand. He had his manly face on – a sort of half glare mixed with a smile that curled up only the one side of his mouth. He usually used it when he saw a digger or tractor. Then he nodded his head three times; not the full nod, but an inclination of acceptance.

At eight o'clock, the strange party rode off. After all the build-up I thought they'd roar off down the driveway in a cloud of bike smoke, but they barely broke two miles per hour. Two quads, four people, seven legs between them. They still had several hundred miles left to go on what was to be Peter's last journey as sadly he died later that year.

'Well, that's another first,' said Will. 'I wonder what else might happen to them on the way to Cornwall?'

Merlin had to lie in a darkened room for a six-hour nap to get over the motorbike excitement. I thought about Tommy and the many assorted siblings, both real and imaginary, all day long, until my mother arrived with one of her "buy one, get one free" supermarket deals.

The offers were a ploy, of course – really she wanted to talk about Tommy. We often got a BOGOF deal in times of emergency. But she was strangely quiet compared with the previous evening. Perhaps she was hoping I would raise the subject of my rather strange relatives. I didn't. She carefully placed the anticipated advice note on the dining room table and, as she left, she qualified it with a few of her stock phrases.

'Just a few thoughts, love,' she said. 'Take no notice of me... You know how I worry... Now I'm not interfering...'

I watched her leave from the safety of the house. My mum, a vision in beige, walked up the garden path towards her car. Even though she was in her seventies and had been driving for decades, she was still unable to coordinate her feet and hands at the same time to steady a vehicle. One of Ellis's recent comments came to mind, 'She's not particularly safe behind the wheel. She drives everywhere in second gear.'

After spending too long trying to reverse in a space large enough for an aircraft, she positioned her little silver car like she was ready for take-off. Then, she drove away at the predicted thirty-three miles per hour. This was the speed she adopted for all situations, whether on the motorway, country lane, roundabout, or simply driving into the garage. She could park in an instant by slamming on the brakes with no warning.

The advice note was telling us to get rid of the inflatable paddling pool we had put in the garden for Sasha, as rats could fall into it and give you Weil's disease. There was no mention of Tommy, Nick or Peter – but I bet she was tempted.

Chapter 18

The Yorkshire Dales

Later that summer, Sasha and I travelled to the Yorkshire Dales to visit Tommy. Busy falling in love with the scenery, I didn't notice until it was time to leave that I had also been busy becoming fond of my parent.

Tommy's little home, his chicken shed as he called it, was nestled in a tiny hamlet, surrounded by magnificent moorland. Beyond the village, the gorse, known locally as The Whins, gave a yellow hue to the hillsides. The landscape was almost deserted, apart from several hundred sheep. This was a stunning place to live and I could see why Tommy had chosen to settle up here, but it was in stark contrast to my other birth parent's city dwelling.

To Sasha's delight, Tommy had a secret room, which was hidden behind a bookcase in true Harry Potter style and it was going to be her bedroom. That first night she climbed happily up the ladder onto the top bunk bed, exhausted after the long train journey. When she was safely tucked in, I walked outside to have a smoke, perching on the wall of the small bridge as the sun set, enjoying the views and the peace. All I could hear was the sound of the trickling brook below me and the faint bleating of sheep way up on the hills. As the evening settled, a flight of housemartins swooped home. Inky blackness soon followed, folding itself over the moors, quietening the river, but heightening the screeches of the owls in the nearby wood. I heard the door of the little chicken shed close. Footsteps.

Tommy joined me on the bridge. Hanging his arms over the wall, he stared down at the now almost invisible river.

'You coming back in? There's cheese and biscuits. I got some Wensleydale in, there's a creamery not far from here…'

'Tommy, I've never met anyone else who likes cheese as much as I do.'

'Well, you'll find that girls tend to emulate their fathers.' With his elbows on the bridge, he bent his head down so that his chin rested on the backs of his hands. 'I wish you'd give up them fags.'

'I wish you'd been around earlier, I'm a bit long in the tooth now for advice.'

'I'm not telling you to give up smoking because you're my daughter, I'm asking you to give up because you will, eventually, kill yourself.'

The silence that sat between us wasn't uncomfortable.

After a while he spoke again. 'I'm sorry I wasn't around for you. I just wanted to try to make it up to Marie by finding you, so she got you back in some way.' He paused. 'I know I never can... my actions all those years ago were unforgivable. But I've told her, you know. I told her when I met her recently on that night in Sheffield that we've got a daughter to be proud of.'

We stayed on the bridge, and let the river beneath us run its course.

Back inside "The Chicken House", Tommy made a supper of Wensleydale and whisky and we settled ourselves for our own bit of storytelling. I enjoyed hearing about Tommy's life. We sat up way into the night, until the fire had burnt away, leaving the last of its embers with just a hint of red in the grate. He told me all about his travels across the world. He seemed less guarded now we were on his patch.

'You know, the first I'd heard of you and your twins' arrival was a few weeks after you were born. I got into terrible trouble with the army. I was marched in front of my officer, told to tie a knot in it, then given three days of extra duties. That was the way they dealt with these things.'

'Did you ask about us?'

'Yes, of course, but I was told to shut up. I wasn't allowed to speak,' he carried on. 'Can you see how I appreciate you giving me a chance to explain – coming all this way. It must be costing you a fortune with the visits to us all.'

'You're worth the effort and the journey,' I replied.

Sasha and I felt strangely at home with Tommy. Sasha was enchanted with the secret room, delighted with its bunk beds and had slept well in what she called the "hush-hush" bedroom. She was just as enthralled with all the ducks that Tommy kept, especially the ducklings. What with the wonderful countryside, Radio 4 chatting away in the background of his kitchen and – of course – all the cheese, the location was beguiling. But it was Tommy's company that I really enjoyed.

Over the next few days, we dashed about all over the place in his little blue car. We went to beaches and waterfalls; we drove across mountain roads, hardly able to see out of the windscreen because of the mist that lurked around us, distorting the trees and shrubs, making them appear larger than life in the gloom. The bleakness of the moors was captivating, the scenery so similar to Southern Ireland.

Our last journey with Tommy found us heading towards the train, but we weren't feeling quite ready for home. It was unexpectedly difficult to leave him – but that's what happens when you let down your guard. Tommy had worked his charm on us, too – it was obvious to see why Marie had loved him. My birth father had made his mistakes but, at that moment, I chose to recognise his more endearing traits, those that were apparent to me now, those of a gracious, benevolent man.

Nevertheless, after a couple of days of being home with my thoughts, I rang Marie to check my parentage.

'Of course there's no doubt. We were engaged.'

'Oh dear, I'm sorry, Marie. I just had to check out that you are absolutely sure that Tommy is my father.'

'Whatever next! There's absolutely no doubt. I can't believe you're asking me this. My God! What do you take me for?'

'I'm sorry, it's just… he seems so lovely, I find it hard to think he abandoned you.'

'Well he did, love, he did and no doubt about it. I've lived it. He went off to South East Asia in the army, so he wouldn't have any commitments. That's what happened. I was a Catholic. I was seventeen and I was naive. There was no contraception for me – I left that to Tommy. I thought he knew what he was about.' Her voice softened. 'But it was more than that – I loved him, I truly loved him. He is lovely, isn't he, Dervla?'

'He's a charmer all right, I'll give you that.'

'What he did for me, by finding you, is the kindest thing anyone's ever done for me,' she said.

It was a very exciting time. There were so many people to get to know. Marie's now grown-up children, Patrick, Carla and Helena came, each in turn, to stay at the farm. First to arrive was Carla. We watched as she deftly manoeuvered her two children and all their luggage off the Friday evening train. Her dark hair and big green eyes made her look even more beautiful than I'd remembered. The black cap that was perched jauntily on her head suited her well. She didn't have the appearance of a woman who had been trapped in a carriage with two young children for several hours. Holding her sticky-fingered toddler in her arms, she made steady progress across the platform, Her other boy, Keiron, lagged behind, grizzling as he tried to cling onto her leg.

'Hello, love,' I said, 'you all right?'

'I am, love. But the kids have driven me nuts getting here.'

Although it must have been torture for her, a city girl, to stay with us in the village that time appeared to have forgotten, she tried hard not to let it show. We lived in a rural location without even a shop, we had an erratic heating system and animals inside the house. Our world couldn't have been further from hers. We were short on child entertainment too; we didn't have a Wii, or a PlayStation or the seemingly essential Xbox. The mobile phone only worked if you hung yourself – and it – out of an upstairs window, and, as Carla remarked with surprise, there were no street lights. Instead there was the constant hammering from the blacksmith's forge. By the time we had battled through another day of trying to entertain her electronically-minded children in the middle of nowhere, Carla and I were both exhausted.

Merlin, however, showed no signs of fatigue – he misbehaved daily, and was enjoying himself hugely, trying to scare the Northerners. At night, he tried to creep into Carla's bedroom by limbo dancing under the gap at the bottom of the door. He finally succeeded in gaining entry by discovering a new trick – jumping up and placing his front paws on the door handle while pushing the door open with his nose so he could snuggle up next to her.

The constant stream of customers, relatives and visitors were all accompanied by torrential rain, which made it almost impossible to go anywhere. We eventually braved the wildlife park, but the animals were cold and hiding from the weather.

'Where are the lions, Auntie Dervla?' asked Keiron.

'Too cold to come out of their den, and who can blame them when they haven't got umbrellas?' In fact, the only wildlife we witnessed on that day's outing was native to these parts – two deer, a crow, and a dead badger, spotted later, on the way home.

'It's boring just driving around,' he said.

'Yes, it is. Let's go to the café.'

'Can we, pleeeese? I'm starving,' he pleaded.

Keiron was starving because of my stubbornness. Every evening I had refused requests from Carla's children for takeaway food. Instead, I had gone in pursuit of making the perfect casserole from unidentified meat that I found lurking in the bottom of the freezer. After the unsuccessful trip to the wildlife park, though, a mix of guilt and desperation sent me out through the never-ending storms to drive to the local Chinese takeaway.

In the mornings, we collected our eggs from real live ex-battery hens that roamed freely about the place. Carla's only previous dealings with poultry had involved a trip to Kentucky Fried Chicken, and I was sure they didn't use free range. I teased her endlessly, telling her that we had recently eaten one of the sheep. We were clearly both products of our upbringing, nurture not nature. Carla's idea of primitive was if the shops in Sheffield shut early on a Sunday.

By the third day, Carla was feeling like she needed the familiar security of the city.

'Where's the nearest shop round here, love?' she asked.

'Three or four miles, love,' I replied.

Oh my God, that's awful!'

On Sunday afternoon I unloaded Carla and all the children at the train station. We were a little early for the train to take them back home, but the place was already heaving. The station master paraded down the platform, looking important.

'The carriages are packed,' he told me. 'It's going to be a job to fit any more on.'

'She has to go,' I replied, glancing at Carla. 'The kids want to go home.'

'She'll have a job – it's always the way with these special rugby trains.'

When the train arrived, passengers were crammed together like refugees, looking like they were trying to flee from the West Country before winter set in. Faces were pushed up against the misted glass of the doors.

'We'll never fit, love,' Carla said, looking doubtful.

'Yes you will, you have to. Leave it to me.'

I worked my way to the front of the platform, pulling the toddlers behind me. Carla followed with the bags and the buggy.

'Sorry, sorry, love,' she said as she squeezed through the grumbling crowds.

The carriage doors opened, but nobody got out.

'I need help!' I called to the rugby-goers, who jostled and joked, swigging cans of pre-match beer. 'It's vital my sister gets her kids home.'

Like a parting of the waves, the crowd moved to the sides of the doorway. Huge hands reached out to help manoeuvre Carla and the kids towards the overloaded carriage. Burly men lifted her, the children and the luggage inside, I pushed from the rear, forcing them through the open doors into a space that wouldn't have passed an inspection, out of harm's way, just before the doors shut.

The conductor's whistle blew its final signal, and I watched with relief as the fully-packed train headed off to Bristol, then the North.

I was sure Carla was relieved too. She surely couldn't face another meal without chips.

But, despite our differences, I was enchanted by her. Carla was the very best thing to happen since the birth family's arrival into our lives.

Chapter 19

A Chat with Marie

Of course, while I was getting to know Tommy, I was also continuing to get to know Marie…

'Hello?' said the voice on the other end of the line.

'Is that you, Vernon, how are you?'

'Oh, Dervla, nice to hear from you. D'you want Marie?'

'Yes please, if that's okay?'

'Well, it is, 'cept we have two of the grandchildren 'ere tonight. They've run her ragged all day, so she's in the bath having some peace. And she isn't very happy since the incident. I expect she'll tell you all about it.'

'Incident? Well, don't bother her…'

'No it's okay, it's just she's a bit worn out, she can't stop cleaning because of her COD.'

'OCD, I think you mean?' I said.

'Appen it's summat like that. Hang on.'

There was a clatter as he put the phone down.

'Marie, love, are you decent? Phone… it's your Dervla.' Then he called 'You'd better tell 'er what happened.'

'It's all right, love,' Vernon finally shouted into the receiver, 'she's here now.'

'Thank you.'

There was a kerfuffle; noises of muffled conversation.

'Hold on Vernon, I'm just putting my hair in a turban. Hold on, can't you?'

'Marie?'

'Love?'

'It's me. Are you all right?' I asked

'Yes, 'cept I just got out the bath. Sorry love, we've got Jed and Keiron staying. Keiron's five now, but looks thirteen. Bless him, he'll be a tank of a man, but our Jed is like a dwarf.'

'You shouldn't say that these days.'

'Why?'

'It's not exactly politically correct...'

'Well, whatever you want to call it, he isn't right growth wise,' she replied.

So Keiron's like a bulldog, and Jed's more like a whippet?'

'Perfect description, love.'

We giggled.

'How've you been?' I asked.

'Suicidal after my hair cut last week. Jesus, when I came out of the salon I felt desperate.'

'What happened then?'

'Janine, the hairdresser, was going through trauma. Her husband Tim drowned a few months ago.'

'Oh dear, how awful.'

'Yes, all that. And I was sympathetic and all, but every time I asked anything about her well-being she cried and cut more of my hair off. With every cut from them scissors of hers she was more distraught. When I finally plucked up enough courage to ask if Tim had been given a good send-off she went into a decline – left me with a receding hair line, two bald patches and no fringe. I only went in for a trim.'

'Annie Lennox has a short hair cut. She has an amazing face.'

Marie paused.

'She does love, she is very lovely,' she sighed, 'but you're missing something. I'm not like feckin' Annie Lennox, am I? I haven't got her face.'

'Right…'

'Anyway, it's okay,' she continued 'because Vernon has ordered me two fringes off the Internet. They're only £2.75 each. He's ordered them from Hong Kong!'

'Hong Kong? But you're blonde.'

'And?'

'Most people from Hong Kong are dark haired. Anyway, how do you apply them without a wig fitter or hairdresser. With Velcro?' I asked.

'Clips.'

I felt desperate.

'That won't work Marie.'

'It has to, I'm going to our Courtney's wedding a week Saturday.'

'Hat?' I suggested.

'It'll be too hot.'

'Better to be hot than wear a wig that's completely the wrong colour for your skin,' I replied.

'It'll be fine. I'm off to town tomorrow to get a back-up fringe. Vernon's looking on the Internet to find me a place locally.'

I couldn't believe what I was hearing.

'You have such shops do you, in Sheffield?' I asked.

'Eh? Don't you?'

'Round here I could get you some sheep food, a castration band for a male lamb, a bale of silage and a pig feeder, but back-up fringe? No chance.'

She moved the conversation on.

'I feel terrible for those people near you, on the Somerset levels, with the floods. It's a national emergency.'

'It is,' I said. 'Even more of an emergency than being without a fringe. Mind you – imagine their trauma: house flooded, cows floated away downstream, Noah gone without them. Then the cruelest blow of all, Vidal Sassoon's shop in Bridgwater evacuated because all the fringes have been washed away.'

'Very funny' she said.

A few weeks later, I saw the photographs of Marie at the wedding. There wasn't a wig or hairpiece in sight. In fact, she looked as always, fantastic.

CHAPTER 20

DISCUSSING CELEBRITIES AND AN INVITATION

Over the next few months, Marie and I got to know each other better with the help of British Telecom. Our calls were becoming a Friday-night standard and Marie usually came up with something to surprise me. One evening though, Marie rang with an even bigger surprise up her sleeve than usual. What she told me put the fringe wig into the category of trivial.

'So, are you saying then, Marie, that Frank McCourt might be a cousin of yours?'

She paused. I could picture her looking from side to side. Then I heard her padding away, quietly shutting the door that led from her kitchen. She was barricading *Jeremy Kyle*, and Vernon, into her front room.

She lowered her voice, then whispered conspiratorially into the receiver.

'Kind of, love. His mother, Angela, was apparently my mother's second cousin twice removed.'

'Is this fact or rumour?' I asked.

'I haven't thought about it, Dervla,' she sighed. 'Everyone in Limerick is related.'

I could still hear the TV blaring away in the background; the *Jeremy Kyle* credits' music seeped out under her front room door into the kitchen. She changed the subject.

'I'm spring cleaning, Dervla.'

'But it's November!'

As she talked into her walkabout phone, the noises of her scrabbling about in her kitchen resounded down the line. Marie sounded like she was becoming increasingly agitated in her efforts to skip hibernation and begin spring cleaning. I heard the metallic scraping of pots and pans along the work surfaces as she woman-handled them into the sink. Had I asked her one question too many this time? Had I sent her into a compulsive cleaning overdrive?

'Well, we aren't related to Terry Wogan, are we?' I carried on. 'He was from Limerick.'

'Of course not. Who do you think we are? He's from a different part of the city, the affluent area. He isn't from Keys Park.'

'Is your mum still there?' I asked.

'Yes, she is, in one of the only remaining houses in her street. Most of the others have been bulldozed, but she won't move. God, that would make her have an angry fit.'

'So nearly the whole neighbourhood has been demolished, but she's still there?'

'Yes… it's not a modern look around the place, the house needs decorating, but she has her family near. She can't face moving at her age,' said Marie.

'Is she all right? It can't be healthy staying there.'

'Ha then,' she snorted in retaliation. 'We aren't quitters in our family. Stubborn perhaps, you'd call it.'

She sighed and I heard her throw a pot into the sink. I didn't believe it was a calculated response, more that she was exasperated with my questioning.

'Anyway,' Marie went on, 'She's your gran, and she wants to meet you.'

'But she isn't my gran really, is she?'

'Well, she's my mother and I'm your mother, what more evidence do you want?' Not surprisingly, Marie sounded cross. After all, I'd challenged my birth link back to the previous generation. It would be enough to bring any of us up short.

I could never forget that, although Marie and I had been busy with our phone conversations, we still had thirty-six years to catch up on. It wouldn't be possible to fill in the gaps. If you'd missed the years, you couldn't just imagine them back. That said, even though we were separated in the past, by now I knew that we were bound forever in the future. What was missing, I decided, was the nurturing that binds generations together. The link to Marie's family was still tentative. The ties that forged these links hadn't been strengthened by love. Growing up, my links had been forged through another family's toil, wrought with them through years of experience and growing together. My feelings for them hadn't grown weaker since the new family's arrival; in fact, they had become stronger than ever. In the past, I had taken the security they offered for granted. This was my epiphany: realising just how important my extraordinary adoptive family had been.

'Sorry, that's not what I meant,' I said. 'It's just that we don't know each other. It could be tricky.'

'We don't do tricky in my family,' Marie countered. 'We haven't got time for such luxuries! It won't be like that, she'll love it. She's been asking about you.'

'Really?'

'Yes, of course, love. We're all meeting up, and you're invited. It'll be in December in London. My brother Aedan will be there. He was adopted too. He doesn't know his mother or most of my siblings. I knew him until he was three years old, then we were separated.'

I tried to take in the enormity of what she'd just told me.

That's a massive thing for him,' I said. 'And his mother.'

'He's lovely,' said Marie.

'Can I bring Sugar with me so that she can finally meet you?'

'Bring whoever you want. Sure, there'll be loads of us, so it makes no difference. My family knows how to party. It's going to be brilliant.' Her voice dropped, as if perhaps she was being overheard. 'I have to go. Sorry, love. I'm going up the club with Doreen and the taxi's due in fifteen minutes. I have to put my face on; ring you tomorrow?'

'No, don't worry, talk next week.'

I dialled Sugar's number. The answer phone message assured me that Sugar would get back to whoever was calling just as soon as she could.

'Hi Sugar, it's me, Dizzy,' I burbled at the machine. 'Could you come to London in December, please? There's a big Irish family reunion. I'm going to meet them all. Even Marie's mother – my gran. Anyway, I'm going to be meeting the whole family.'

Sugar rang back later that evening.

'Oh, Dizzy, of course I'll be with you. Can you give me the dates? I'll have some time off from work. Wow, missus! You're going to meet your gran. That's wonderful!'

'I had a wonderful nan. I certainly don't need another, nobody could match up to her. But thanks, Sugar. I'll book the hotel, it's just so flipping good to hear that you'll be there.'

Two paths had led me here: one well-trodden, one barely walked upon. The first was my life with Paula and Terry, Nan and Ellis, Will and Sasha; the other, the new family. In my mind, the two paths still remained separate. But rather than moving in parallel lines, like the tracks made by horses at the plough, these lines seemed to be moving apart from each other. It was as if the horses were not walking side by side, not working in harmony, but straining away from the furrow.

I would have to go to the party, but I'd already made up my mind that I wasn't going to enjoy it.

Chapter 21

The Irish

Sugar and I travelled to London on the Friday-afternoon train, made a dash across the city on the underground, walked the last two miles and arrived at the party at gone 9pm. The Irish family reunion had started at lunchtime, so celebrations in the pub were well underway.

Before us, the fog of nicotine cleared to reveal a riot. The inside of the pub was filled with horizontal layers of smoke that drifted lazily towards the ceiling lights, where the grey, poisonous fumes collected before finding the air vent and escaping. We stood, momentarily framed in the doorway, and stared. It wasn't hard to make out Marie's siblings among the crowds – all drinking, most smoking, and some squabbling; a gathering organised so that Marie could meet her brother, also adopted – he was separated from Marie when he was a baby and would be encountering his siblings and his birth mother for only the second time.

I studied this tribe of mine, who all looked so similar, as they pushed and jostled to get the attention of the lone barman. This was the first time I had seen Marie's family as a whole. That scene from *Star Wars* – the one with the creatures in the cantina – flashed into my mind.

Mayhem.

Sugar touched my elbow.

'Go on, you're fine,' she whispered. She nodded towards the direction of the room. When I hesitated, she pushed me forward, into the merry confusion.

Marie, looking as pristine as ever, spotted us amidst the smoke. She tottered over on heels that looked like they should be confiscated on the grounds of health and safety and marched Sugar and me in to meet her family. First, we were introduced to Marie's brother, Uncle Liam, who was leaning on the side of the bar, surveying all around him.

'Are you Marie's girl?' he asked.

'I am,' I said.

'Well, come on here and let me hear all about it now,' he said, winking at Sugar.

Liam looked more like a man about to sell us scrap metal than a relative offering a seat on the sofa.

'Come on and sit down here next to me,' he said.

He planted himself on the nearby sofa and patted the empty spaces either side of him. Sugar and I duly positioned ourselves. We were next to the speakers and the Irish band was in full swing. The siblings were all joining in; singing, dancing, and falling in front of us, holding onto each other for love and balance.

'Would you look at yourself, Sinead. God help you,' called Liam, raising an eyebrow in the direction of a dark-haired, tiny-looking woman who was having trouble walking in a straight line. To give her credit, though, she could still dance.

'That's my sister,' he told us. 'Look at the state of her, and it's only just past nine. We love her, but she can't take a drink, not like the rest of us.'

'Sinead!' He beckoned her over with an animated hand gesture. 'This is Marie's daughter, Dervla, the one that got taken.'

Sinead moved unsteadily towards us. She tried to focus on my face, but she was so drunk her eyes went in different directions.

'Derv,' she hiccupped, 'Dervla… I've never heard of you. Come and dance.' And she staggered away.

'She has a great job that one, she works for Alcoholics Anonymous. You'd never think that to see her now, would you?' said Liam.

'Does she, really?' asked Sugar.

'No, she's a teacher.'

Liam's green eyes twinkled with delight and mischief. Drinks flowed. He peered at me, getting closer, leaning in to scrutinise my face.

'There's a look of our Bridie in your bulging eyes,' Liam whispered. 'She's a feckin' card.'

It was impossible to speak at normal volume, so conversation was mostly shouted, but, what with the overwhelming noise, we only caught snatched sentences and odd words.

'Drink, Dervla? Cigarette, Sugar? Oh, you're gorgeous gals, and sure you look like one of the family, Dervla. You know,' said Liam, 'I'm surprised your mother had any children. Before you came along she was planning on joining the convent, taking the vows of chastity, but your father obviously got to her before the nuns did.'

This family didn't believe in spreading themselves out to maximise the space in the room. They preferred to huddle. They sat next to or leaned on the two massive speakers, and for full effect, as the evening wore on, they also lay on the carpet, within feet of the band. This meant we had noise from every angle, reverberating off the nearest solid object. This, for us, happened to be Marie's chest, bouncing in time to the music.

The other outsider in the room was Adean, Marie's long-lost sibling, and we found ourselves standing together. We were scrutinised, then thrown into the tumult, both of us struggling without our familiar props to lean on. But we had each other for life jackets so, as the evening wore on and our new family got ever more inebriated, we gladly clung onto each other for help.

And when the mood changed, Marie handled everything with good grace. The first we knew that something had happened was when we saw Marie striding toward us, clasping her handbag in front of her. Her lips set in a tight line.

'Every time I meet up with my sisters, it's the same. I knew my lipstick had gone missing and my foundation. When I went into the ladies, there they were, Bridie and Sinead, plastering themselves in my expensive make up. I'd gladly give them anything I own– they just need to ask me.'

'It wasn't me, Marie,' Sinead called over, 'I'm not a thief. It was our Bridie. I don't want your feckin' foundation. Wrong colour, see?' She pointed to her own complexion and stroked her cheek with her fingers.

'You can take it,' said Marie, unzipping her handbag and turning it upside down. She emptied its contents onto the table. As one determined bunch, her sisters descended, snatching up the make-up, grabbing the little black pots and tubes from each other, squabbling over the eye shadows, blushers and lipsticks, and the "feckin' foundation!"

'Don't you want this, Marie?' asked Bridie, helping herself to one of the little tubes.

'You give that back, Bridie. I'm the eldest, give it!' Sinead attacked from the rear. She wrapped her arms round Bridie's neck and jumped on her back; when she turned her face to us, she was laughing.

I wondered if every one of their Saturday nights was like this.

But Sugar was going with it. By now, Uncle Liam had made her one of his own. They sat together on the sofa and supped Guinness, as Sugar told Uncle Liam all about her own Irish family.

'Come with me, Dervla.'

It was an order not a request. Marie grabbed my arm.

'Come and meet your gran.'

Sugar got the hang of what was happening and her hands pushed me onwards until I stood in front of Marie's mother – presented like a package of what could have been. Small and dark-haired, she had a smile for us, but few words. In her early seventies, Marie's mother was the same age as my adoptive mum, Paula. She was still pretty, but her life had been hard. After seventeen pregnancies, death and miscarriage and the adoption of three of her children and grandchildren, somehow she had managed not to be emotionally shut down.

'This is my Dervla, my daughter,' Marie said.

Her mother half turned towards me. 'I've heard about you. It's a good thing,' she said, not making eye contact. 'I'm glad she has you in her life.' She nodded towards Marie.

Those were her only words. Then, she turned her face away.

Later, I watched her from across the room; she was standing alone at the edge of the crowd where the noise and chaos melted away. She was looking at her family, but not really observing – alone with her thoughts. I wondered if others noticed.

Next morning, Sugar and I left before breakfast. We needed to go and find some quiet place away from all the relations that were also staying at our hotel. We travelled down in the lift in silence, watching the numbers above the door light up. At the second floor, it stopped. The doors opened and Bridie and Sinead joined us. We travelled silently on again. Sinead stared at her reflection in the lift mirror. First, she fluffed up her hair so that it draped across her face, then she pulled it out from behind her ears and let her fingers run through its thick darkness to its ends. She looked back at me from the mirror.

'Jesus,' she said. 'How do you both look so glamorous this morning? And there's me and Bridie here, looking like a couple of wolves.'

CHAPTER 22

A NIGHT OUT

But I hadn't met all the relatives yet. Next I was summoned back to the bungalow to meet Marie's younger sister Rosheen, who hadn't managed to make the reunion in Greenwich.

On entering Marie's house, I was nearly knocked out by the smell of Domestos. She was being more frantic than usual in her effort to eradicate every last speck of unbleached anything. She darted from one room to the next, waving her dishcloth, even more energetically than usual. Marie's battle to overcome her cleaning obsession clearly wasn't working. Her house was so clean you could have performed surgery on the kitchen table. She greeted me at the back door, bleach bottle in hand.

'I've been up since five, love, preparing for my daughter.' She grinned and took my face in her Marigold-clad hands and planted the expected antiseptic kiss. 'I cleaned out all the cupboards, scrubbed the skirting boards and bleached the floors,' she said.

'Marie, you'll wear yourself out – it smells like a sanatorium in here. I expect Vernon's worried he could be next to get a good rub down.'

'What, with my weak chest, you must be kidding,' she said.

She glared through to the adjacent room where the TV was blaring; I followed her gaze, glancing from the tiny kitchen into the next room, where Vernon, in his normal position on the sofa, was engorssed in the *Jeremy Kyle Show*.

Marie gave a withering look.

'That telly drives me mad.' she said loudly. 'I wish Vernon would get off his backside and do something. I hate the telly. In my opinion that Jeremy Kyle is evil, look at his face all contorted with anger.' She shot a look in the direction of the TV.

'Vernon, walk the dog... NOW!' she shouted. But Vernon, his expression unmoving, merely stretched a hand out to reach for the remote control to turn the TV sound up so he couldn't hear her.

Since my last visit, Marie and Vernon had bought Radar, an English Springer Spaniel. All my warnings against getting a dog that would be better suited living on a farm or out shooting had been ignored.

'But he's so sweet, Dervla, and he was going to be put down,' was all Marie could say. I'd explained to Marie about my problems with Merlin. I was worried that they'd made such an inappropriate choice of breed of dog, living, as they did, in a bungalow with no garden.

Radar was bouncing from armchair to sofa, frenetic with lack of exercise and training. Vernon was oblivious so I offered to take him for a walk.

When the dog and I got out of earshot of the house, we had a serious talk.

By the time we returned, he was walking to heel. It was short-lived. As soon as I opened the back door he pushed past me, bounded inside and landed on Vernon, spilling his mid-morning coffee all over the white sofa.

'He needs more walks, Vernon. He needs to go off the lead, and you ought to enrol him in dog-training classes,' I said.

'Oh, he's all right.'

Vernon, now watching *Homes under the Hammer*, obviously had other things on his mind.

'I thought you had a dog behaviourist round recently,' I said. 'Have you done what she advised?'

'Aye? No, that's Marie's department.'

'The whole family has to do it!'

Marie had gone off to her job as a care warden, dealing with the elderly of Sheffield, so I took the dog out again, and we played fetch the pensioner on the tiny patch of grass behind the houses. Poor dog, living here when he should have fields to run in and pheasants to retrieve.

Occasionally, we saw Marie dashing by, going quickly from one bungalow to the next. It was a small enough estate for me to be able to hear her voice as she stood on the pensioners' doorsteps.

'You all right, Bob, love? Did the Meals on Wheels arrive or shall I cook you an egg?'

'Have you got your Sudocrem, Beryl? You don't want that chaffing to come back again.'

At one point, I saw Marie talking to a policeman. An ambulance was called and there was much disruption amongst the residents of the other little bungalows. When Marie eventually returned, finished for the day, I was waiting for her, sitting on the patch of grass outside her home with Radar. It was still early afternoon, and Marie didn't look like she had been to work. She was made up like she should be going to a film premier, wearing a faux fur coat, high heels and black velvet trousers. She looked as though she should be mingling with the stars or be jetting off somewhere altogether more glamorous than her surroundings. She looked as if she really didn't belong on this housing estate.

Her words, on the other hand, were very much grounded in the grit of the pavements of the North.

'I've had her from number three sectioned. It's not safe leaving her alone with medication,' she said.

'Will she come back?' I asked.

'Hope not. She's delirious poor lamb. She thought I were Esther Rantzen this morning.' Marie delivered this line without humour – it was a tragic situation. She dealt with difficult situations like this every day.

'How's the training going with my little angel?' Marie bent down to stroke the dog.

'It's going to take a while, Marie…'

The dog behaviourist had given sound advice before taking her £180 fee from Marie, but I now told her the truth about the dog's prospects.

'Marie, I don't think it's fair to keep him. He's not got enough to do. Unless you both commit to walking him several times a day and training him, he'll always be destructive.'

'Do you mean Vernon?'

We laughed, but she knew that I was talking sense.

'Vernon won't help me, Dervla.'

'Well, you clearly haven't got time, have you? You need to both be firm with Radar and work with him. If you can't, he'll have to be re-homed.'

Marie said nothing, but looked down sadly at the little spaniel. It'd been her desire to have a dog of her own. I felt sorry for her.

'See how it goes, then,' I conceded.

Later, Marie's sister Rosheen arrived in time for some beauty preparation for a night on the tiles. Like the rest of Marie's siblings, she came fitted with the required, broad Limerick accent. We were all dispatched to Carla's house to get ready. After witnessing their mysterious rituals, I decided that these women were world class experts at slapping on the face paint.

I watched in awe as Carla, Marie, Rosheen and Helena expertly applied layer after layer of foundation, eye make-up and false eyelashes, and curled their hair. They were transformed.

'Your turn, our Dizzy.' Carla came towards me with the curling tongs. 'Just going to do you up a bit,' she said. 'You need a bit of make-up now, love. When you get to a certain age you need a bit of help.'

'Not where I live you don't.'

Carla applied far too much blusher. I was glad Sasha couldn't see me – not exactly the maternal role model for her I had in mind. After being squeezed into one of Carla's dresses and a pair of heels, I put aside all thoughts of my wellies. I was ready for the north.

We clip-clopped our way through Sheffield's streets, going from bar to bar, our laughter getting ever more raucous as the vodka washed away our inhibitions.

It was surreal, going to a night club with your mother. My West Country mum and I preferred lunch and a dog walk. Where we came from, mums didn't get to go clubbing with their children.

In reality, though, I was loving this partying in Sheffield. We were all out to have a good time. I didn't know anyone and nobody cared. To say that the man who approached me and asked for a dance was odd-looking would have been doing him an injustice. He had slightly convex eyes and a receding hairline.

He was also wearing black boots with a small heel and he carried a man bag. In real life I wouldn't have danced with anyone that carried a handbag, but this was Sheffield, so anything went. I wasn't sure how to respond to a strange man wearing inappropriate footwear who kept standing on my feet with his boots. After a few times though, I'd had enough.

Carla, Helena and Rosheen stole me away to the ladies.

'Ooh, our Dizzy, look at you. Get his cowboy shirt. He loves you.'

'Yes, well, I don't know what came over me; the man is obviously insane and shouldn't be out without a helper,' I coughed.

'Oh Dizzy, you're just like us. What a laugh you are, you aren't really a snob.'

Marie, glamorous as ever, appeared as if by magic from one of the toilet cubicles. Rummaging in her bag, she produced more weapons from her make-up case, which she gave to Helena and

Carla. They pinned me to the sink and started applying extra layers.

Marie proceeded to strut her stuff until the wee small hours. For nearly sixty, she could still pull 'em. We were set for hours of fun ahead. In fact, so serious was the party mood that Marie ordered twenty-eight tequila shots! But then her mobile rang.

'Hello. Who is this?' She shot us a look; then her expression changed.

'VERNON! What do you want?'

She held the phone at arm's length and made impolite suggestions with a cocktail umbrella.

'What d'you want to be doing, phoning me up now? Yes, there is more John Smiths, it's hidden in the larder.'

Five minutes later, he rang again. Carla, the most sober of us all, took the call this time.

'All right, Vernon, love? Yes… yes… she is behavin', you daft sod. What's she going to be doin' at her age. What? EXCUSE ME…? This is my mother you're talking about!'

Marie snatched the phone.

'For feck's sake, Vernon, what is it this time?'

Marie listened intently, the mobile tucked under her ear so that her hands were free to take a shot of tequila. She half closed her eyes, her brow creased.

'The TV remote is on the mantelpiece,' she said, eventually.

But Vernon was clearly so concerned about mislaying the TV control that he couldn't manage any longer; he needed assistance. We sent Marie home in a taxi.

On returning to Carla's, we staggered upstairs. Carla, Rosheen and Helena got into a single bed. I stood by the door, holding its frame to steady myself. It was like watching sardines fit into a tin.

'Where am I sleeping, Carla?'

'In here, love.'

'Don't be ridiculous! That'll be four of us.'

'Well, yes, love, there's nowhere else.'

They were laughing at me.

Rosheen then told me how it was, her Limerick accent penetrating the quiet night; her words, although funny, stabbed at my conscience.

'Get in the feckin' bed, Dizzy! Jesus, you're so spoilt. Back in Ireland there would have been twenty-three of us in a bed this size. Now get in the bed and shut the feck up.'

And that was it, that was the truth. Life here wasn't like my comfortable life back home where everyone had enough beds to go round.

Helena had fallen onto the floor and passed out, so I stepped over her and curled my whole body onto the pillow without a fuss. I daren't complain there was no blanket. At six in the morning, after only three hours of pillow contact, I couldn't stand it. There'd been more laughing than sleeping, apart from Helena who was comatose.

It wasn't funny anymore. My lack of sleep had left me in need of a humour transplant. I staggered along the landing to the loo and, on my return, noticed two-year-old Jed wasn't in his room; he had crept in with his dad.

Seizing the opportunity, I scrunched my body up into Jed's car-themed bed, which was designed for a two-foot-long toddler. The Formula One stickers raced round my head, reminding me of other kinds of transport options. They also prompted me to remember that I had a train to catch at ten o'clock that very morning.

An hour later and Jed was peeling open my eyelids with his fingers. I woke to see a toddler in blue tracksuit bottoms and socks, staring at me – a stranger in his bed.

Well, this was a new experience; surely we were all old enough to know better. Besides, the social worker had said nothing about situations like this.

Chapter 23

Marie Gets Run Over

Safely back in the West Country once more, I busied myself with more attempts at cooking. This time it was bread making I was intent on conquering. Unfortunately, the few loaves that initially materialised from Daphne's oven resembled house bricks more than anything nourishing. Daphne just wasn't keen on sustaining a temperature conducive to the slow rising of yeast. As there was a mounting loaf production line to grapple with, it was a while until I phoned north.

'Hi, Marie, it's me.'

She sounded so delighted to hear from me, she almost sung her reply into the telephone receiver.

'Hello, love.'

'Have you been all right?' I asked

'Yes, fine thanks,' she paused. 'Well, actually no… I mean I am now, but Vernon ran me over last Wednesday, the daft prat.'

'What! Really! Oh dear, what happened?' This wasn't going to be the quick call I'd planned.

'We'd only been to the supermarket but, on returning home,

I just got out of the passenger seat of the car to direct him back into the parking space. As he was reversing, Vernon pressed the accelerator not the brake. He can't work his hands and feet at the same time.'

'And?'

'AND the passenger door flew open so he hit me in the head with it. I fell to the ground, but he carried on driving.'

'Oh no! Are you all right?'

'I'd just got back onto my feet again when he drove forward, knocking me down for a second time.'

'Did you go to hospital in an ambulance?'

'AMBULANCE? I wish. No, worse than that, Vernon drove me.'

I gulped, trying to stifle the giggles.

'Oh dear, I'm sorry.'

'It's all right, love. It were funny, I suppose.'

'You should learn to drive.'

'ME? Oh no, not after the last time. The driving instructor refused to learn me; he dropped me off at the side of the road and Vernon had to come and get me.'

'That bad was it?'

'Yeah, I'm not the correct temperament to learn, it's me hormonials.'

'Your what?'

'My hormonial levels, that's what the doctor said.'

'Have you had HRT?'

'Oh yes, tried it all. My doctor's lovely. He fancies me you know, he always looks at my chest.'

'Um, right… Well, I'm sure he does, it's a very splendid chest; I don't expect he can help it.'

'I'm on such good terms with him that I only have to make a call and he has antibiotics ready for collection, what with my past chest problems, you see,' she said.

'Hmmm.'

'Anyways, I'm well enough now. I'm going to one of my psychic readings on Saturday afternoon.'

'Shame you didn't have one last week,' I replied, 'it could have predicted Vernon running you over.'

'You all have The Gift, all my children have it.'

This was the first I'd heard about our 'Gift'.

'I don't want it,' I said.

'Well you have it and that's that, I'll do some cards for you. After the reading we're goin' up the club with Doreen on Saturday night. I hope she isn't on one, I'm not in the mood for her. She can be a right snob sometimes, you know, and I hate snobs.'

'Hmmm.'

She could be referring to me.

'Well, I'm glad you're okay. Speak next week then?' I said.

But she wasn't letting me go quite so quickly.

'Have you heard from Tommy?' Marie asked.

'Yes, an email anyhow. He's away at the moment.'

'Again? Where now?'

'Australia.'

'Humph... lovely, I'm sure.'

I tried to move the subject on.

'Are you going anywhere?' I asked.

'Yes, Torremolinos. Vernon likes it there. Personally, I'd prefer somewhere a bit more exotic, like Greece. But he likes Spain.'

'Lovely. I'm sure it'll be warm at least.'

I was desperate to hurry this phone call on now, as I had to collect Sasha from school and time was ticking, but Marie was in full force.

I've had another letter from your mum,' she said.

'Oh good, it's wonderful that you write to each other now.'

'She writes beautiful letters. I'd like to meet her... I could come down.'

OMG! Marie in the country, being real, walking around our

village. Dodging the cow muck in her high-heeled boots, meeting real live people and possibly some ghosts, given her ability to converse with the other side.

'I don't think you'd like it,' I said – 'it's a bit bleak.'

'It'll be lovely to see you again and meet my granddaughter, Sasha. Meet your mum and step-dad, too. Ooh, I can't wait. I'll be down in October then.'

Nonplussed, I drove to school, gripping the steering wheel very hard. I walked zombie-like to the school gates to wait for Sasha to run out to me.

'Sasha, Marie Dishcloth is coming to visit,' I told her. Then I repeated the words, unable to believe it. 'Marie is coming here.'

'Is she nice?'

'She's very nice, and she's your nana.'

My nan isn't called Marie Dishmop, she's called Nanny Paula. Is it the lady you went to meet, Mummy, when you were sad?'

'Yes, it is my love. The lady that was my mummy – but when I was a baby some unhappy things happened to her and she couldn't keep me with her, so she gave me to Nanny Paula.'

'That was kind of her.'

'She is very kind.'

'You would never give me away would you?'

'No, my darling, never, but I'm lucky, I don't have to,' I said.

It was three months until October. I had lots of time to prepare. But could the West Country ever be ready for Marie?

CHAPTER 24

MISS UNTIDY

By now, any illusions I had about Marie and this newfound family being like folk we'd met on a holiday were long gone. It wasn't going to be a case of just keeping in touch by sending Christmas and birthday cards. The past was gaining speed. It seemed as if it was belting up the dual carriageway of life, in danger of screeching up alongside the present. I wasn't sure of anything anymore. Marie's impending visit exacerbated this feeling, and the Boots herbal remedies weren't working. Clearly, this was something that I needed to sort. So, I took action.

The Yellow Pages found me a local therapist to guide me through Marie's dreaded arrival. I'll call her Miss Untidy for the sake of confidentiality. On the allotted day, I wandered up to her front door. Next to it was a double garage with its doors wide open. It looked like she used it to house her junk pile, which was so colossal that she could have filled another house.

Miss Untidy had many letters after her name, all of them engraved into a grubby-looking brass plaque outside her front door. Feeling uncomfortable, I waited for her to answer the bell, hugging myself against the cold.

In her garden, homemade-looking art hung from branches, vying for space with dreamcatchers that spiralled in the late summer breeze. Unfinished stone sculptures lay, their limbs poking out from the grass that threatened to cover them. A strange doll's head, detached from its body, was discarded on a grey, plastic table. When a skinny black cat came to check me out, rubbing around my ankles, I was glad of her welcome.

Eventually, the therapist opened her door. I stared. She was tiny, with a mop of dishevelled hair and wearing a chocolate brown full-length corduroy skirt that had clearly dragged on the floor so that all the dirt worked its way up into the folds of fabric. Above this, she wore a baggy cheesecloth blouse with a grandad collar. At the end of her bare feet were long, dirt-encrusted uncut nails.

As surprised as I was at her appearance, I was even more alarmed at the amount of stuff lying about the place. Inside the dimly-lit rooms lay books, discarded food wrappers, and overflowing cat-litter trays. Old bits of computer equipment jostled for space. This was where junk went to die; it clung onto tables, chairs, cupboard tops. Piles of magazines teetered over the edges of windowsills, looking like they were trying to leave. Briefly, I wondered whether someone with so many hoarding issues was qualified to help others. I didn't like mess anymore than Marie did and, at that moment, I could have done with her and her faithful dishcloth to give Miss Untidy's house the once-over.

Reluctantly, I followed her through the house, picking my way across a floor covered with books and boxes over which several more cats slumbered. To my eyes, the possessions looked like debris, but I guessed that these were Miss Untidy's treasures.

It was the rat-sized holes in the skirting board at the bottom of the stairs that almost stopped me in my tracks. But I'd got this far, so I continued following the therapist up the winding, rodent-chewed staircase that smelled of damp and decay. Freud would have had a field day.

I put my hand out to steady myself as we climbed, but there

was no rail, just huge, gaudy portraits that hung, neglected and at an angle, all the faces tilted slightly to the left. Perhaps they were pictures of old clients.

By now experiencing serious doubts about her professional ability, I thought I'd better set the record straight from the off. So, as we entered the therapy room I made sure she knew where we stood.

'I don't want any of that quiet therapy where the therapist doesn't speak, mind. I'd like your opinion, please. I need you to be proactive.'

Miss Untidy nodded, but didn't smile. This could be hard work. She sat me in a comfy chair and set the clock to an hour. This room didn't hold any junk – just the two chairs, an alarm clock on a small table and a book shelf containing many papers on therapy techniques. I stared at the flaking skirting boards and thought they could benefit from some gloss, easily distracting myself from the job in hand. We sat in silence. Eventually she began going through the terms of our engagement; 'this is to be confidential,' she told me – she would only share information if she thought I would harm myself or others. I thought I might harm Miss Untidy if she kept up this unfriendliness, I'd found it difficult to ask for help – to even get this far had been a bit of a risk, so right then I could have done with a friendlier welcome.

'I'm sorry I was a couple of minutes late,' I said, by way of making conversation. 'I couldn't find your house.'

'It's your time, Dizzy. If you want to be late it's up to you.'

I immediately felt told off and patronised – not a great start to our relationship.

'Would you like to start by telling me why you have come to me, why you now feel the need to reach out?' she asked.

I spilled out the whole tale. I had nothing to lose – I remembered I wasn't there to make a friend.

'Well, it's because I was adopted,' I said, 'and recently my birth family tracked me down with the help of a private detective. There are loads of them. They're Irish and of a very excitable nature. I only wanted to have a look at them, but now they think I'm part of their family. The problem is that I already have a family and I'm feeling rather overwhelmed by it all.'

Miss Untidy nodded, made sympathetic faces and handed out tissues. Occasionally, she penetrated any uncomfortable silences with helpful comments like "Hmmmm" and "Really?" presumably to encourage me to expand on my explanation.

'Plus,' I said, 'my birth mother Marie thinks she is a psychic and – even worse than that – she's coming to stay.'

'I see. That must be very difficult for you, Dizzy.'

Mid nose-blow, I glanced up at her.

'Well, that's why I'm here.'

'I'm hearing what you're saying, Diz,' Miss Untidy said.

Since when did we become so pally? Diz now was it?

'You need to put this other family of yours into little boxes and get them out when it suits you.'

I stared at Miss Untidy's uneven teeth. Feeling angry with her, I thought how distracting it was to be watching a mouth full of molars that would look good on a mule.

'How do you reckon I can do that?' I asked.

I knew I was being miserable and difficult – knew it wasn't fair on her. I tried again to explain.

'Look – they keep phoning and arriving. I don't want to be rude, but the thing is, well… the thing is, um… I don't think I'm getting on terribly well with my birth mother.'

There was a pause. Miss Untidy seemed pleased at this early revelation. She had been asking the right questions, her training was obviously paying off.

'And my birth father arrived with a half-brother I didn't know about, and, on the way to our house, he lost his friend's false leg on a bypass.'

Miss Untidy tried not to look shocked; she had adopted the serene smile employed by welfare professionals when they don't know what to say.

'I see, and did they find his leg?'

'No, it's somewhere between Keynsham and Bristol,' I told her.

At the next visit, the local environmental health officer was in Miss Untidy's hallway, laying out tiny trays of blue food that was appetising to rodents. This second meeting got off to a better start; I was pleased she had asked for help from the environmental health department for her problems. I was obviously making headway in making her address her underlying early parental separation.

'How have you been getting on since we last met, Dizzy?'

'Merlin bit one of our customers,' I said.

'A challenging week, then?'

Cordelia, as she'd told me to call her, had no idea of the complications I faced.

'Just a normal week.'

'Hmmm. Anything else you would like to bring to the table?' she asked.

There was no table; obviously, the rats had eaten it.

'On Friday, Will bought an old army lorry and had to take the gate off to get it down the drive. He drove it across the lawn and got it stuck. It's been there for three days. Merlin is very distressed, because he thinks a permanent intruder is waiting to pounce on us out of the cab. He can see the lorry from the window if he climbs onto the back of the chair. He barks at it all day.'

'Hmmm… right, will it be moved?'

'We'll have to get another lorry in to move it and…'

I was becoming increasingly worried about what I was putting her through – I wondered if Miss Cordelia Untidy would crumble under the pressure of my problems.

'And later that morning I had to pop to our daughter's school as she'd forgotten her PE kit. I was horrified when I found her. An older boy had tied her to the school railings with a skipping rope – especially as the rest of the class and the teacher had gone back into the classroom for circle time.'

'Hmmm, tricky.'

'Actually, I can't stand it anymore. Living my life is messing with my mental health.'

We both drew breath.

'We also might have a YTS trainee starting with us who will have to board three nights a week, because there are no buses to take him home. Plus, our friend Prue might be moving in as she's losing her accommodation.

'Have you got the time and space for these people?'

'No!'

'Why do you feel you have to take on other people's problems?'

'Well, people have been very good to us. It's awful to be in a situation where nobody will help you; I'm very lucky,' I continued – I didn't want to sound like a victim.

'It's not your problem, Dizzy. You can't save everybody.'

I glared at her… It was all right for her – she might live in a messy house, but she probably didn't have to deal with a messy life.

I decided to challenge her. 'Well, imagine if we all turned our backs the whole time,' I said.

'What would you do if your friend was going to be homeless and asked you for help?'

'There is no need for anyone to be literally homeless these days in the UK,' she replied.

At this point, I wondered which planet she lived on.

'If you turn your back on other people, you're being selfish – that's the way I've been brought up. When we were growing up, we had everybody living with us, people we didn't even know came for Christmas.'

'It's fine if you can cope with it, Dizzy, but you have to look after yourself or you end up no use to anyone.'

'But so many people ask us for help, and,' I added, 'if I tried to say no, I'd feel guilty.'

She sighed.

'You manage an awful lot more than most would take on,

what with the new family, your job, the forge at home… and that dog.'

It was clear Cordelia didn't like dogs, and this worried me. She did, however, have an overworked cat that was stressed out trying to keep up with all the vermin. Leaning back in her chair, she sighed again.

'But the very worst thing,' I continued, 'is that we may have to move, because there's a new management team taking over the estate where we live. We went to a meeting about all the changes that are going to be happening. They might not be able to renew our lease now.'

'Have you not got security of tenure?'

'No, hardly anyone on the estate has, but with the old team that didn't matter. The rest of Will's family are okay; they have three generational succession leases on their farms.'

'But you've never received one, even after all these years?'

'No.'

'Are they going to evict you?' she asked.

'Not as such, but we don't feel secure there now. It's awful, this feeling that they could give us two months' notice to leave and there would be nothing we could do about it. This fear of not getting a proper lease is hanging over us. We can't bear to leave our home – we've been there for over twenty years – but we might have to.'

'Home is very important to you isn't it Dizzy?'

She was right – it was. Whatever stress I felt about Marie's visit, it would be nothing compared to having to leave our lovely home.

'We've put down roots there. Plus, we don't know what we'll do with the business if we move. It's everything.'

'You're going to have to start standing up for yourselves,' she said.

It took Miss Untidy a while to get her message across, but after a few weeks, it sank in. Will and I were going to have to think about our own needs and say what we wanted more clearly – and soon, even Miss Untidy was going to have to manage without me. I was almost sad when I finally left her, in her now rodent-free accommodation.

CHAPTER 25

BEYOND THE VEIL

We collected Marie and Vernon from our local country train station early one October evening. On the surface it was all smiles and "How are you?", but underneath I was dreading the moment when I'd have to introduce my birth mother to my mum.

Marie floated down the train steps in full make-up, hair scooped up into an immaculate bun. Seeing her on our turf was alarming. Dressed in her leather coat, she looked out of place beside the farming community in their wax jackets and wellies – a lone and glamorous figure, soon to be dropped into the field that contained our house. I wondered if we should drive her quickly to Vale Farming Supplies to get her some overalls.

As soon as she alighted from the train, Marie spotted Sasha. She sped over as fast as her stilettos would carry her – all heels and lipstick.

'Sasha, sweetheart,' I whispered, bending down, 'that's Marie, Marie Dishcloth. Say hello.' Sash smiled up at her. Marie could hardly contain her excitement at meeting Sasha. She dropped her handbag by her side and bent down to gather up into her arms the granddaughter she had never seen. Meanwhile, the now abandoned Vernon was still aboard the train, grappling with his own and Marie's huge cases. He was struggling to get himself and all the luggage down the train steps.

'Oh love,' Marie said, now on Sasha's level, her arms stretched out in front of her so that she could clasp Sasha's tiny hands in her own. 'Aren't you gorgeous? I've been desperate to meet you.'

She reached into her handbag and pulled out a small shiny parcel. She pushed it towards Sasha.

'Here you are, Sash,' she said. 'A present from me, all the way from Up North. We have fantastic shops where I live.'

She beamed at me, threw her arms round my neck and then went over to Will. He held out his hand, tentatively, but that was a waste of time – it wasn't Marie's style at all. Instead, she pulled Will to her in a binding embrace and didn't let go. Sasha clasped the parcel tightly. Her eyes asked me if she could open it.

'Wait until we get into the car,' I said.

We manhandled Vernon, the enormous load of luggage, and everyone else into our tiny Mini and, with some trepidation, we set off for home. Marie sat in the back seat, looking out of the window, taking in the scenery.

'Isn't it beautiful down here, Vernon?' she said.

'Aye, it is that. Not many houses though.'

'We like it like that,' said Will.

'Well, it wouldn't suit Marie,' Vernon said. 'She'd go mad without a Peacocks.'

'Take no notice of him, Dervla. I love the countryside.'

'Well, granted you like looking at it from inside the car with the heater on,' replied Vernon.

'I'll have you know, thank you very much Vernon, that I was brought up near fields. We used to play out for hours.'

Marie tilted her chin up slightly, turning her head away from Vernon, and stared out of the window.

Sasha, sitting between them on the back seat, fretted at the sticky tape on her present. After some time picking at the gift, she uncovered a small blue jewellery box. As she lifted its lid, she found what was hidden inside: a delicate silver necklace with a tiny horseshoe charm.

'Ooh, my favourite, horses. Thank you very much indeed.'

Marie had chosen correctly.

'You're welcome, sweetheart.'

When we eventually pulled up in the farmyard, it was obvious from the barking inside the farmhouse, that Merlin, a step ahead of us as usual, had been lying in wait for our return. As we climbed out of the Mini, his barks were interspersed with a pitiful howling; the noise seeped through the gaps in the windows and underneath the front door.

'That sounds like a big dog, Dervla. Is it friendly?' asked Vernon, pulling the cases out of the boot.

'Um, well, once he's accepted you,' I said, looking at Vernon, who looked back at me nervously. 'The most important thing is that you show absolutely no fear.'

Merlin was waiting behind the front door. As soon as Will pushed it open, taking advantage of the tiny gap, our dog leapt at Vernon, placing his paws on his shoulders and pushing him back against the porch door.

'OH MY GOD! Ger 'im off me!'

'Merlin, get down!' Will heaved on his collar. 'Sorry, Vernon, that's probably it now – he won't give you any more trouble. It's just his initial enthusiastic greeting.'

We made our way into the house with Marie, Sasha, Merlin and the cases.

'There we all are then,' I said breezily. 'Safe inside. Who wants a cup of tea?'

We went through into the kitchen, and I reached into the wooden dresser for the mugs.

'Sugar, Marie?'

'Oh no! Thanks, pet. Not since my new diet.'

'What about you, Vernon?' I turned towards him, but he wasn't there. 'Where's Vernon?'

Everyone, including Merlin, stared at me innocently.

'Oh dear,' said Sasha, 'we've lost Vernon.'

'Could you have a look for him, please Will?' I asked. 'He must be out in the porch, or gone to fetch something from the car.'

Marie and I made the tea. After a short while, Will came back and delivered his unfortunate verdict.

'Can't see him anywhere, he must have gone for a walk in the woods. I hope he doesn't get lost or he might fall down a hole – get snatched by Ginny Greenteeth.'

'Who's that?' Marie demanded.

'Bog fairy,' Will said, giving Sasha a wicked wink.

'Don't be ridiculous,' I said. 'He's not going to fall into any bogs. But as he doesn't know his way about, and it'll be dark soon, perhaps you should give him a ring on his mobile, Marie.'

'Shall we call the police, Mummy?' asked Sasha.

'Not yet, love.'

Marie found her phone, which was switched off. She pressed button after button, working out how to turn it on to make contact with Planet Vernon.

'Vernon. VERNON! Can you hear me? Where the bloody hell are you, I've come all this way to see our Dervla and you've gone and got yourself lost in a forest.'

She held the phone in front of her face and pressed the keypad, randomly stabbing at the buttons.

'OH MY GOD! It's gone straight to his messages. Suppose he's hurt. He's been acting strange for a while. Suppose he's had a turn. Suppose he's dead! What will I tell his children?'

'Don't worry,' said Will. 'Let's have a quick cup of tea, then Dizzy and I will have a proper search.'

Merlin stood up, arching his back in the air like a cat, and yawned. He gave us a wilting look then padded away quietly. He was up the stairs in a trice. The mere mention of a search had sent him back to bed.

'I've got a lot of farming family around here,' said Will, keeping a straight face. 'We can get tractors and diggers. Ron from the pub could bring his terrier in case we do have to dig Vernon out of a bog.'

'Stop it, Will,' I said.

'And of course,' Will carried on, ignoring me, 'there was that sighting of a big cat in the village recently. Betty saw it when she was putting her bins out.'

'Don't be so dramatic, Will. Everyone knows Betty drinks far too much sherry. Vernon probably thinks we have a village shop. I expect he's gone to get some chocolate,' I said.

Marie looked very serious. She bit her bottom lip. 'Vernon doesn't like chocolate,' she said.

We sat in silence, except for the sound of the odd slurp as we tried to drink our tea.

'Did you hear that?' asked Sasha.

'No. What?' I asked.

'Sssshhh,' Will said.

We all sat very still, mouths poised over the tea mugs, to listen.

'Mummy! There's Vernon, look...' Sasha said, pointing to the dining-room window.

We all looked. Vernon was staring in at us, mouthing words that were inaudible through the only double-glazed window in the house. He raised his hand in the general direction of the porch.

'I'll go,' said Will.

He opened the door, calling out into the garden to Vernon.

'All right, mate? We thought we'd lost you. You coming in now?'

'Where's that dog?' Vernon shouted. 'He hates me. Best I stay out here for a bit 'till it calms down.'

Marie scraped her chair back from the table. 'For God's sake,' she muttered, 'only a mother could love 'im. He shouldn't be allowed out on his own.' She joined Will at the front door. 'Ger in 'ere you daft prat,' she called through the doorway. 'It's only a dog. Ger in 'ere NOW! Or I'll ruddy kill yer myself.'

Vernon managed to get as far as the porch. He stared through at us, gripping the door frame for balance. Eventually, Will nursed him into the safety of the dining room.

'Sit here, Vernon,' Will said, pulling out a chair.

I bustled about giving tea and sustenance. We did hear a movement from the upstairs bedroom, but it was only Merlin turning over in his sleep. He'd had his fun.

Chapter 26

Mum and Marie Meet

We drove to our local pub for dinner, where we'd arranged to meet Mum and my stepdad, Al. We pulled into the pub car park and Mum was already there, sitting in the car with Al. Her mouth was set firm, but she brightened when she saw us. My mother had been consistent in her message to me over the past few months.

'Nothing can stop our love for each other, and we've got more to go around,' she had said.

Will, Sasha, Marie, Vernon and I got out of the car and walked down the slope to greet them.

My mum held out her arms when she saw Marie, and they hugged. Marie's high heels made her tower above my little mum, who looked small and depleted, but once mum's mouth went into action there was no disputing who was going to be in charge that night.

There was a lot of polite chat at first, which all seemed very formal. We need not have worried, though, because once Al got an eyeful of Marie, he took us all down to his level.

'Oh aren't you lovely! You look like Dizzy, come here and let me give you a hug.'

Without waiting for permission, he tried to grab hold of Marie, who held her elbows firmly in front of her.

'I see where Dizzy gets her boobs from,' he said.

'Al, behave!' Mum spoke through gritted teeth,

Marie was a match for him, though. She'd met his sort before. Taking hold of his arm, she led him into the pub.

What a strange party we must have seemed. To all intents and purposes, we were just a family out for a meal, yet what a history we'd had to bring us to this place.

Sasha clung to her Nanny Paula's hand as usual and they talked about school. Mum rummaged in her brown leather handbag for treats, pulling out a colouring book and a bar of chocolate.

'For later, mind,' Mum told her.

Will said nothing, bringing up the rear in his silent, solid way. Vernon clopped along in his cowboy boots, whilst my mum tried to understand his remarks, made with a strong Sheffield accent overlaid with a slight speech impediment.

'Well, this is a shock, isn't it Praline?… I mean, Pauline, Paula. Dervla certainly looks like her mother… um… I mean, Marie.'

'She does, yes. And I've heard a lot about you, Vernon,' said Mum.

Mum and Vernon went for a cheek-to-cheek kiss; but bumped noses and giggled. Once inside the pub, the matriarchs sat opposite each other.

'How was your journey, Marie?' Mum asked.

'Oh, all right, Paula. Vernon gets free travel on the trains and that's a blessing, I'd kill myself if he had to drive me all this way.' They laughed. 'I'd love to live down here, though. Hasn't Dervla got a beautiful home?'

'Will and, um, Dizzy, have worked hard to get it up to scratch,' said mum.

'Oh sorry, Paula, I just can't get used to calling her Dizzy.'

'It doesn't matter,' said Mum. 'Nobody minds.'

Mum nipped to the loo, maybe to compose herself, but I

couldn't be sure. Marie leaned across the table and took my face in her hands.

'Let me look at you darling, you're so like me,' she whispered.

As soon as I was able, I dashed to the loo so that I could see for myself. On peering into the mirror I was horrified to see that Marie and I had done our hair in exactly the same way. It was her staring back at me from the glass; I wouldn't escape her now.

Mum ordered her usual, which was salmon with no sauce, and Sasha had the same. The men ordered mixed grills and Marie asked for a salad. I didn't want anything, but lived in hope that I would muster an appetite for the cauliflower cheese I'd ordered.

As Al had lived up North, we were glad of him to distract the early conversation. He and Vernon discussed the merits of Leeds versus Sheffield. I glanced at Mum. Small and demure, she was immaculately turned out in a top that covered up her chest and upper arms, sensible but well-cut trousers, flat leather shoes. She was also wearing a silver brooch left to her by my nan.

Marie, on the other hand, looking glamorous, was in a plunging Primark top in bright pink. Black leggings made her legs look even longer, all set off with galactic heels. Her jewellery was plentiful. Sasha, as usual, was wearing green, in keeping with her camouflage phase. She had been wearing the same clothes for months, even though she had other brighter garments in her wardrobe.

It was good to have her there. She was too young to say the wrong thing, but if she had done, she would have been quickly forgiven. The adults would have laughed and looked at each other in a knowing way. So, yes, her presence was a great distraction.

In fact, the whole event was fine and weird, not horrible and weird. I got tipsy in the corner and longed to be at home in bed. It was like being on a works do where you couldn't let your hair down. Mum picked at the salmon and Marie picked at the salad and we all carefully avoided the subject of Tommy. Vernon had been through enough of late without Tommy being mentioned.

Marie talked about her other children and grandchildren, and Mum made her laugh with stories about my teenage exploits, which included stealing road cones, a flashing yellow beacon and some window boxes from outside a bank after a night out. The others made headway with their main courses as more tales were told at my expense to entertain Marie; this time, mum told her about how I'd crashed two cars, shaved my head and went out with a boyfriend who was a taxidermist – whilst I stared down at my plate and pushed the cauliflower cheese about. Marie reached over and stroked my cheek.

'Dervla looks like my family. Her sister, Helena, was a card when she was growing up. We had right trouble with her, didn't we, Vernon?'

'Aye.'

Vernon mumbled through a mouthful of mixed grill and flashed Marie a look. He gulped it down when he realised he was meant to expand on the story.

'Ha, she was a proper tinker was our Helly.'

The silence sat heavily between us. Our table was cluttered with discarded red napkins and empty glasses; apparently a party had been going on.

'Does anyone want pudding?' I asked.

I was trying to keep it normal, move it along without disaster.

'No thanks, my love.' Mum smiled and gave me a knowing glance. Composed, professional but kindly, like when she was a teacher.

I looked to Marie, who dabbed her mouth with a frayed red napkin.

'No love, I'm stuffed, that was lovely.'

She looked down at my untouched plate.

'You need to put some flesh on your bones, love. Look at you, so skinny.' Marie paused, she tilted her chin up slightly; her teeth were straight, I noticed, she had good teeth.

'I was only eight stone when I fell for the twins, Paula. Of course, I didn't know there was going to be two of them, no scans in them days. It was a shock when another little one arrived after Dervla. Still… she has had a wonderful life with you, I wouldn't have worried half so much if I could have known where she had gone.'

'Well, she's been hard work at times, Marie, but we all love her ever so much. Dizzy, her brother Ellis and the grandchildren have all made our lives.'

'Oh, I can see that, I'm so grateful to you, Paula. You see you never stop wondering…'

Marie looked away, out of the window; she was somewhere else a long time ago, remembering.

'No, after I lost my babies, I…' Mum went on, her voice quieter now. 'Then Dizzy came along when we thought we would never have the chance of another child.'

Marie clasped my hand beneath the table.

'I can make sense of it now,' she said. 'You were meant to have her, Paula. I brought her into the world and you cared for her.'

That surely was the biggest thank you there could be between two women. Like a puppet, dangling helplessly in mid-air, on strings of silver thread that they were both holding, I was in the middle. The thread to Mum was taut and solid; the thread to Marie was looser, but still there – an invisible umbilical cord.

Mum and Marie obviously had a lot they wanted to say to each other in private. They told us they would like to meet on their own the next day.

'We'll drop you over, Marie. Eleven o'clock, Mum?' I suggested.

'Yes fine, Vernon can go to the workshop with Al and look at the engines, so Marie and I can have a proper chat. We don't want the men around, do we, Marie?' said Mum.

Vernon nodded in appreciation of the fact he could look at model steam engines tomorrow. Working on the railway for donkey's years hadn't quelled his appetite.

Mum and Marie had hit it off in a spectacular fashion, as I'm sure I would have done – if Marie was someone I'd just met on a holiday we would probably have become friends. But, back then, on that night of the meal, I was still keeping her at a distance – stopping myself from knowing her properly.

*

On the way home, Marie said that if she could have picked a mum for me she would have picked Paula. 'She's a wonderful woman, I think she's fantastic. So kind, and funny. It's been important for me to meet her. Thank you, Dervla.'

I turned to face her, 'No problem, Marie. We had a lovely evening, didn't we?'

'And Al, what a card.'

'I'm sorry about him.'

'No love, he's great.'

Will had been even quieter than normal. It'd been a strain for him having Marie and Vernon – the strangers that had unintentionally caused havoc in our home for the last sixteen months.

Sasha was dozing in the back seat of the car. Marie put her arm round her shoulder, she studied her little sleeping face. The moonlight danced on the wet road ahead of us, sending its brightness to light our way home.

CHAPTER 27

MARIE AND THE AFTERLIFE

We were all relieved to be home. A sleepy Sasha disappeared off to bed, while Will disappeared into the kitchen to have a cigarette. I made a pot of strong coffee and carried the tray through to the front room, where Merlin had wasted no time in choosing to bestow his attentions entirely on Marie, who was sitting in his leather chair. With the skill of Fagin, he took up more and more of her space, edging into it inch by inch without her really noticing. Although, he was unsuccessful in evicting her, he spent the remainder of the evening sharing her chair, snuggling up to her as she tried to drink her coffee. Every time she stopped stroking him, he pushed his head into her hand, reminding her of her task. Marie kept up a constant petting of Merlin; she didn't seem to mind that he was encroaching on her personal space.

By bedtime, he had almost swamped her completely. He made it all look so effortless. With his head perched on her bosom, he rested his front legs on her shoulders but, as he was so long, his back feet were still on the floor, stretching himself out so that nobody else could get near her.

Merlin wasn't so sure about Vernon, the Sheffield lone ranger. Clad in cowboy boots, he looked like he should be in a band singing country and western songs. All that was missing was a guitar. In fact, Vernon was lucky that his prized footwear, all shiny now and smelling of leather polish, had been returned to him. Shortly after his arrival, he had stood in something that he really shouldn't have stood in and I had spent a fair while cleaning his boots out in the garden, cursing under my breath.

When at last the evening's small talk was over, I explained to Marie and Vernon that we'd had to put them in the walk-through bedroom. There was nowhere else unless they could fit into Sasha's single bed, but she was already there, surrounded by images of dolphins and fast asleep. So, if we needed the loo in the night, we would either try to have a wee out of the window, or walk through the room they were going to be sleeping in.

Our quirky accommodation didn't lend itself to privacy. Also, I told them, they would be sleeping in the room that Merlin found most desirable, in his own double bed in fact.

'What would you prefer?' I asked. 'Merlin outside your door, crying all night to be let in, or him getting into bed with you straight away?'

'Oh, he's all right love, let him in. Since my Radar was re-homed, I've really missed him. I'd love a dog of my own,' said Marie.

'He farts a bit, I'm afraid.'

'I've had twenty years of Vernon now, so a dog won't worry me!'

'I hope you sleep well,' I said.

'Well, it depends if there are any spirits that make themselves known to me.'

'Spirits?'

'Yes, Dervla, I have 'The Gift' you see. I told you before – you'll have inherited it, too. All my other three children have it, but Helena is the only one that has accepted it.'

'Right… okay.'

'Sometimes I get a psychic vision, sometimes it's a message,' Marie said.

I made for the door.

Later, when I went upstairs to check on Sasha and say goodnight to Marie and Vernon, Merlin followed me – he was never far from my heels. He pushed the spare room door with his two front paws so that it opened, then he shyly peered round the bedroom door, eyeing up Marie and Vernon. He moved closer, tiptoeing across the wooden floor, making the lightest of sounds on the pine boards. Merlin stared at his double bed and the strangers who lay on it. He then disregarded the fact that other individuals were on his patch. With his only two brain cells lightly rubbing together, it seemed a rare spark was ignited and it dawned on him that the easiest thing would be to pretend Marie and Vernon weren't there and get into bed as normal. So he jumped up, flopping down on top of Marie, temporarily flattening her.

'Merlin, come on, come here,' I said. He lifted an ear, but then chose to ignore the request completely. Letting out a weary sigh, he snuggled closer to Marie, nuzzling into her neck with his nose. She didn't wake.

Needing the loo at three in the morning, I intended to slip as quietly as was humanly possible through the guest bedroom. I was surprised to see the light on full blaze; I paused. Vernon looked very small in the bed. He had adopted the fly-catching, open-mouthed position of a man who had consumed too much Newcastle Brown Ale the night before. His newly polished cowboy boots were cast to the side of the bed. The bottom half of Marie was by now nearly completely covered by Merlin.

With his head on the pillow between her and Vernon and his nose level with Vernon's snoring mouth, he seemed to be guarding her in case Vernon should attempt any funny business. Marie, however, was sat bolt upright in the bed, half-concealed in pink Primark pyjamas, with her black dressing gown collar turned high up to her neck. This gave the overall alarming effect that she had kind of slid down inside it. She remained outside of the duvet, purple fluffy socks covering her feet and disguising her webbed toe. Even without the make-up, she was very glamorous. Her right hand was placed on the wall. I stopped in my tracks to the bathroom and stared at her.

'Are you all right, Marie?' I whispered. 'What are you doing?'

Marie had her eyes closed, but was speaking very slowly; not exactly in tongues, but in a distant voice.

'I'm… talking… to… the… spirit… world… Dervla. It's… your… Will's… Aunty… Marjorie.'

Oh blimey, that was all we needed.

'Oh, okay then,' I said, sarcastically. 'What's she saying?'

'A… bad… man… came… on… a… horse.'

'Anything else?' I asked.

Marie opened her eyes, blinking, as if woken from a sleep. Her speech returned to normal.

'Oh, you know, chatting away. She's ever so friendly.'

I stared at Marie, realising instantly that my birth mother was, in fact, a lunatic. I nipped to the loo, then stomped off downstairs for a sherry. If it wasn't surreal enough having her to stay, now she had informed me she was mystically given. I eventually got back into bed and woke Will.

'Marie is talking to your Aunty Marjorie,' I whispered.

'She's dead.'

'I know that, but it makes no difference to Marie. She has powers beyond the veil.'

'It's because she's from up North. They're all strange once you get past Stoke-on-Trent. She's obviously deluded,' replied Will, a southerner of the dyed-in-the-wool variety. He turned over and went straight back to sleep. I gave him a sharp kick.

'Wake up, Will. WILL! What are you going to do about it?'

'I'm going to go back to sleep, and I suggest you do the same,' said Will. 'Ghosts aren't real, so don't start worrying about them as well.'

For an hour or more I lay in bed and thought about Marie

in the room next door. Shutting my eyes tightly didn't make the image of her talking to dead relatives go away, it was just another unsettling thing to happen in the already long list of peculiar events that this last year had brought.

Despite Will's matter of fact dismissal of the spirit world, I wasn't convinced. In all our conversations we had never mentioned Marjorie to Marie; we had had more urgent ground to cover. Marjorie had lived at the farm with Will's uncle for thirty happy years. And she had been, as Marie said, very friendly and chatty.

Over breakfast, Marie went into more detail about her visions from the night before.

'A bad man came on a black horse,' she informed us.

'Would you like more porridge, Vernon?' I bustled about.

'No thanks, pet.'

'A double murder, Dervla,' Marie said.

I paused, the Marmite-covered toast hovering in front of my mouth.

'It happened on this farm hundreds of years ago,' she continued.

There was absolutely no way she could have known about this. We already knew about the murder, originally from rumours told by inebriated locals at the pub, then from a chat with the land agent – who'd had a word with the estate historian. but we still couldn't be sure if it had taken place at our house or in the cottage down the road. All we'd been told was there was apparently a preserved arm of the murderer in the Tower of London, a warning that they had used in those days, we guessed, to put off other murderers! The victims were said to have been pushed down a well. It had given us the heebie-jeebies when we discovered one in our garden, so Will had filled it in with the help of Nathan, the apprentice, whom he had dangled tantalisingly over the hole on a flimsy looking rope.

'Down the well, he pushed the bodies.' Marie's eyes went skyward. My daughter's eyes widened.

It was quite some time before Sasha would sleep in her room on her own.

All the house had a wonderful feeling, apart from the stairs leading to the bedrooms, and the backhouse where the washing machine lived. Sasha and I would skit through as quickly as possible, partly because we both felt it was uncomfortable to be out there, but also because of the mice.

'Mummy, is someone watching us?'

'No darling,' I replied. 'Only the mice are looking at us washing our pants and socks. When there's a missing sock, the mice have taken it to make a nest.'

'Like the tooth fairy?'

'Yes, that's it. The fairies take your teeth and make them into dentures for when you're old, that's why you have to give your teeth up.'

As I sat at the office desk, Marie came and stood behind me; she rested her hands on my shoulders, touched my head, stroked my hair gently. A shiver went through me; it was the first time she had touched me in a tender way.

I served the lunch later that day, trying to make it look easy. All that was missing was my green tomato chutney, so I popped back into the kitchen, leaving Marie, Vernon, Sash and Will to battle with some bread and cheese. When I re-appeared, Vernon fell upon the chutney eagerly.

'Did you make this, Dervla?' he asked.

'Hmm, well, "make" could be a bit of an exaggeration. I chucked it all together, put it in the Rayburn for eight hours and hoped for the best.'

'It looks delicious,' he said, turning to Marie. 'Just like my mother used to make.' He looked back at me. 'Marie has never made me a single jar of jam or chutney, and we been together over twenty year.'

Marie snorted. Vernon took a huge spoonful, scraping it round the Kilner jar, savouring the action. He opened his mouth wide, leaned forward slightly and popped the spoon in, casting Marie a look. This was all very enthusiastic on Vernon's part – he took another huge spoonful, but during only his second mouthful he began to choke, then to swallow frantically again and again, and then he had to do more swallowing than is good for a man. Next, his face twisted slightly to the side, Marie jumped up.

'Oh my God, he's having a stroke,' she said.

'Should we put him in the recovery position?' asked Will.

'Get him some water, love, quick!' Marie shouted. Will was up from his chair and thumping Vernon on the back with hefty blacksmith blows between the shoulder blades.

'God, that vinegar is strong, Dervla. What did you use – Parazone?' Vernon said, regaining his composure.

'Blimey, Diz, I didn't think you were going to serve that stuff. She took the enamel of the Rayburn when she made that, Vernon,' said Will. 'We had to get the darn thing repaired.'

My culinary reputation in doubt, I went back to the kitchen, and thought about the next meal. I had spent ages the day before preparing what was really only a shepherd's pie. With my mind not on the job, I had been surprised at how well it had turned out. It was during the re-heating process that something must have gone wrong. A hormonal reaction from Daphne perhaps or maybe because it hadn't been prepared with enough love. Now the pie was sagging in the middle and looked more than a little disappointed.

I set about the washing up while Marie and Sasha planned the afternoon's shopping expedition. Will prepared to retire to the safety of his forge.

'I can't face a shopping trip,' he said, heaving on his overalls.

'Nor can I,' I said, stacking the pots into the dishwasher.

Marie, Vernon, Sasha, and I spent the afternoon visiting the city of Bath. It was a fair drive, but Vernon had hinted that he would like to go there, after having seen its retail potential featured in one of his many favourite daytime TV programmes. I explained to him, that there was much more to Bath than shops and the odd auction house and, when we arrived, suggested a trip to the Roman Baths for starters.

'I'm not bothered this time, pet, but I could really do wi' a cuppa,' he said. 'As long as there's some shops for Marie...'

Sasha and Marie disappeared into department stores, while Vernon and I took refuge from the shops and the rain in a Georgian-style teashop. We nibbled at Bath buns whilst our coats, slung over the backs of our chairs, steamed in front of the tiny coal fire. Condensation misted up the small leaded window panes, but not so much that we didn't notice Sasha and Marie returning from the shops with an array of huge bags and neat little boxes.

Marie burst through the door, her entrance disrupting the polite mutterings of the Bath tourists. A stern-looking man and his wife glanced over disapprovingly.

'Oh, we've had a fab time,' she said. 'Sash, show your mam what we got.'

Sasha hoisted herself onto the chair next to me, her eyes falling upon the bun, which sat at eye level on the small table.

The man and his wife had plenty more to stare at as Marie started to empty the contents of the shopping bags over our tea table. I hastily moved the cups and plates as bras, pants and assorted clothing descended onto the white linen tablecloth.

'Look, Mummy! Look at what Marie Dishcloth got for me: it's a skirt.'

'Wow, will you actually wear it?' I asked. My daughter had been in combats and muted, camouflage colours for some months.

'Yes! Can I change into it now?'

'Okay, come on then,' I replied, getting up from the table. I cast a look over my shoulder.

'Order yourself tea and cake, Marie, my treat.'

Sasha went into the Ladies with her remaining bag of shopping, whilst I waited by the door. After some time, she emerged. The new skirt was purple and just above the knee, and there were tights too, pink and woolly. Sasha had worn her Converse daps to Bath. Emerald green – the overall look was alarming.

'Gosh, you look amazing!'

'Do I?' she asked.

Abandoning her discarded camouflage clothes in the cubicle, she walked back out to the tearoom where she stared at herself in the mirror that took up the entire back wall. Then she gave a little twirl and ran over to Marie.

Thank goodness, the camouflage phase was over.

Chapter 28

Bleak January

'I've always hated January,' said Will, resting his hand on Merlin's head. 'Something awful always happens in January, but this is bloody terrible. I don't know what we'll do without him.' Will shifted uncomfortably forward to the front of the sofa, resting his elbows on his knees. 'And we can't tell Sash yet, she's going to be devastated.'

'How could this be happening to you, mate?' Will continued, leaning down, burying his face in Merlin's coat to hide his tears. 'We've taken such care of him, he's had the best of everything. There never was such a spoiled dog.'

Merlin had been suffering from lupus for several years now. But recently he'd developed a kidney problem and the rapid decline in his health that followed had only taken a few weeks. He was on the maximum dose of the two types of drugs the vet had prescribed, so I knew that soon, we would have to let him go.

'I won't have him suffering,' Will said. 'As much as it'll break our hearts, I won't let my lovely Merlin feel any pain.'

'Of course not, neither of us would let that happen.'

'How long's he got, do they know?' asked Will.

'A few months, at the most.'

Will left the room, but it was no good going after him; when he was upset or ill he always wanted to be alone. I knelt down in front of Merlin who was, as ever, resplendent. He gave my hand a lick and grizzled to show he wanted a fuss. He could have as much fuss as he wanted.

'Oh, Merlin,' I said.

'I can't stand it, Dizzy, I have to go for a drive,' Will called.

'Be careful, Will. It's not a great idea to drive if you're upset.'

'I'll be all right,' he said, coming back from the kitchen. He crashed about trying to find his keys, then he was out of the front door. After a few minutes the truck started up.

'Come on, Merlin.'

I patted the hearth rug and he came to lie next to me, stretching himself out to feel the warmth. Through the tears, I told him how brilliant he was, how very important. The fire spat and hissed as a log shifted in the grate, hinting at the displacement to come. But still the flames danced their light over the room, giving the illusion of a cosy winter ahead.

*

Merlin was put to sleep on a Monday; it was in so many respects a beautiful day, a beautiful day for others. He lay on the front lawn in the June sunshine, soaking the heat into his old and worn bones for the last time. It's always a long wait when you know the vet is going to end a life. We had been incapable of doing anything else but fussing around Merlin for the last twenty-four hours.

On his last night, he gave up trying to climb the stairs to jump into bed with us. Instead, I brought the comfort downstairs. Together with his other best friend, the little black whippet we had acquired three years before, we kept vigil over our beloved Merlin, snuggling next to each other on one of the larger dog beds, next to the sofa that Merlin had chosen. Wrapped up in a duvet, we watched the eleven-year-old Merlin doze, ready to cover him up with his favourite red woollen blanket should he become cold. Every now and again he'd get up to turn and adjust his uncomfortable self.

*

Summer mornings begin early. On Merlin's final day, the first sun crept through the crack in the curtains and I heard the birds cheerily calling their bliss as they started a new day. I shut my eyes and tried to hold onto the normality that was the start of another morning, pretending that the terrible thing that was about to happen couldn't be real. But, of course, everything had already changed.

By the time the sun had reached its highest point, Merlin's body lay on the grass in the June sunshine, the vet and nurse gone. The little black whippet nuzzled and examined his friend. We let our tears wash over him. Kneeling to stroke and kiss his head, it was unbearable to think of putting Merlin into the ground. I breathed in his smell, kissed him between his ears, and then, pulling my head away, tried to photograph his face with my mind. I thought of the seemingly endless days we'd spent together over the years, Merlin had seen me through some tricky times. Then I covered him in his red woollen blanket, even though he wouldn't be able to feel its warmth.

I desperately tried to hold onto the feeling of Merlin, but I knew that love would never leave me. I had been blessed that he had accompanied me on part of my journey.

When Will and I finally got up to walk back into the house to make yet more tea, I only got as far as the front door. I felt a sudden rush of joy; Merlin was finally free. It was only then that I knew he had truly gone, that he wasn't going to follow. The whirlwind of energy, the spirit that we knew as Merlin, had left us.

The little black whippet was miserable. Over the next few

days, we watched him closely and noticed that on more than one occasion he took his treats and bones to place them on the spot on the lawn where Merlin had been put to sleep. We knew we would have to get him a friend, but right then it was unbearable to imagine who or what could go even a small way to fill the void.

Chapter 29

Leaving

There was more loss in store for us. It had taken us two years, but we had now, finally, come to terms with the fact that we would have to leave the farm. With the new management brought onto the estate, the general feeling was that the best times were behind us. What had once been a beautiful country estate was starting to resemble a theme park; plastic replaced wood and stone. Apparently, customers liked it that way and the new management team needed to boost visitor numbers. Our once-familiar world had become unfamiliar, corporate. We understood only too well what upset this would bring for local families and staff. Some, like Will's family, had lived and worked there for generations. There was little compassion for us with our twenty-five-year occupation of the farm. Nor was there much recognition of the time, love and money we had spent. Forgotten were our battles to obtain planning permission to start the forge in the old dairy at a time when farming had become no longer viable. Through all the uncertainties of the past, we had managed to hang onto the farm. We'd been good tenants; we had loved the place like our own.

We wrote letter after letter, only to be ignored and it became apparent that we would never be able to obtain a proper lease on the house. With only four years remaining on the forge, we were extremely vulnerable. Other people's plans for our home, their visions for the future, were a mystery to us. We couldn't risk what could happen in the long term.

We tried to turn our hearts to stone, without success. So, in one final desperate attempt, we wrote again to the estate. We asked if they would please consider selling to us. After months of waiting, the reply we received was as expected. Will and I sat opposite each other with the letter between us on our familiar kitchen table.

'We can afford a decent place of our own now, Diz, and it will be in the country,' Will said.

Nodding, I pushed back the lump in my throat before trying to speak.

'Yes, yes, but it won't be like this. It won't be like here, with all these memories. Your family has lived in this house since the 1940s. It won't be home.'

'The old estate is gone. They were brilliant to us, but everything changes,' Will replied. 'We'll have to start looking for a place.'

'But, it's not just the house,' I said, feeling desperate. 'What about the business?'

'I may have to carry on from here until the four years are up. It will be awful to see someone else living in the house, while Nathan and I are in the forge, but we can't move it all at once.'

Will, as expected, didn't let his feelings show. Even though he had lived within two miles of our present home all of his life, first farming the land and then turning the old milking parlour that his uncle had used for thirty years into a forge; even though he and his family were truly a part of the estate – we had to go. We started our search.

Some of the cottages we viewed were in strange locations. One was attached to a deserted pig unit – the house didn't smell much better than the sties. Then there was the one where the occupants had clearly fallen out in a spectacular fashion with their neighbours.

'Why the twelve-foot poplar hedge?' asked Will.

Next was the creepy falling-down house that was up for auction. The previous residents had used it as a location to make porn films.

'I won't live here,' Sasha muttered, and strode off to wait in the car.

There were some beautiful places, but they were next to bypasses.

'Too near the road,' we agreed.

There were mill houses, too.

'You can't risk the flooding,' Mum said. We shook our heads.

After viewing an old industrial railway site, complete with ramshackle wrecks of dwellings, that could, with a huge budget and the will of Joan of Arc maybe – just maybe – work, we made our decision.

'We need another forest home,' Will said.

In desperation, I rang Marie and asked her if she could please do one of her readings – whether I believed it or not. I needed some help.

'We can't bear to leave our home, Marie,' I said. 'Please tell me the estate will see sense and give a proper lease on the house.'

'Well, I'm sorry to tell you the news I know you don't want to hear, Dervla, but you will be leaving. You're going – going from the farm, to live by a river. It won't be the place you're veiwing now, but it will be all right, love.'

Like a grief that we knew would seek to envelop us – even though we were trying everything to delay its arrival, we understood that it would eventually find us out. My sadness was not because of the loss of a person, but for a memory of a home and all the people and animals that filled it. And for the links that had tied the house to Will's family for over sixty years. This continuation was important to me; in this house, my roots had been allowed to grow deep.

'We can plant our roots somewhere else, Dizzy,' said Will.

But this was the place where we brought home our baby and raised her, the place where the dogs lived, five in total over the years. Two of them, Merlin and Blue were buried in the garden in unmarked graves, their place of rest, under the honeysuckle, the first thing we ever planted here. If we moved we would have to leave them behind.

Proper sleep hadn't been forthcoming for months. I wandered about, looking at every door frame, floorboard, remembering how I'd stripped the layers of paint from their old knotted surfaces. I could see the dogs racing around the garden, Sasha in the paddling pool on a scorching June day as she washed her bedraggled blue bear. I could hear her laughing as the tiny droplets of water sparkled in front of her face. I could smell the jasmine, honeysuckle and the herbs that told me it was summer. Thyme, mint, rosemary and sage flourished outside our kitchen window, sending their soothing perfumes in to us on a warm night. The bees made steady progress collecting nectar, humming their appreciation, dipping in and out of the centres of the dark purple clematis that had wrapped itself around the deep red rose. Together they had climbed faithfully up the house for thirty and more years. Warmth and comfort, laughter and love.

That New Year's evening, a winter's moon framed the view in the kitchen window, shining over frost-covered woods and hills, making them sparkle. I stood with the lights off, trying to take a snap shot of this view in my mind, so that I would remember it in years to come, when the memory was no longer fresh. The Rayburn sat cold.

I recalled a time when I had been fearful of this place, when, as a girl of twenty-one, with all of my life in front of me, I had found it daunting, living in a house that contained the memories of other people. Since then, I'd grown comfortable in the skin of the house, as if we'd absorbed each other. We had reached that comfortable place, like friends who no longer mind the silences. I couldn't imagine living anywhere else. I knew every inch of the place, from inside the house that we had cared for, to the fields and woods beyond.

Those final few days should have been the hardest times and yet, ironically, I found myself enjoying them, appreciating the security and comfort that a home could bring. When the weather raged outside, sending gusts of wind down the chimneys, when the rain hammered on fragile panes of glass, we were snugly tucked into the safety of the wood that nestled the house. Now that we had to settle ourselves into another forest home, who knew what ghosts awaited us? We all wondered whether it would be possible to settle somewhere else. Sasha said she didn't mind moving – she couldn't understand what all the tears were for.

It wasn't just leaving the house – we had to leave the village too, and that was hard. Our friends, and friends of Will's late mother and father, were still living there – they and our neighbours couldn't believe that we were really going. Will said people weren't bothered, but that wasn't my truth.

That winter's night, when sleep couldn't find me, the memories kept me company. They took me back to a different time, to when it was just the two of us, dancing round the woods without a care. Then a baby came to join us, and our cats, dogs, and a pony to accompany us on our walks.

A picture came to mind. It was a snowdrop-filled spring day. Will was laughing. Merlin, young still, rushed around us, just out of reach. 'I had the best country childhood,' Will had said, smiling. 'We're giving that to Sash now.' Another picture, this time of Sasha, sitting in the bluebells, Mum at her side. Then a new photo of her for every year with the various animals that made up our family's time line. The latest photo showed her as she was now – a beautiful, fifteen-year-old girl with better things to do. Such fun, and such family. I knew now that we had been the lucky ones – that was why I couldn't bear it to end.

It felt like everything in the safe, protected life Will and I had built for ourselves, for Sasha, was being taken away. But Marie's reading was correct, it wasn't the bleak industrial railway place, or any of the houses we had viewed so far that we settled on. We found ourselves another forest home – up a dirt track, deep into the woods. Just next to the river, as Marie had envisaged.

*

We loaded up the last stick of furniture on a cold winter night and, on the 16th January 2013, just seven months after we buried Merlin, we finally left our home of twenty-five years. I paused before climbing into the removal van and called, 'Come on, Merlin. Time to go.'

Chapter 30

Another Forest Home

Our new home was nestled in a clearing in the middle of a wood. You reached it by winding steadily up a little dirt track, and passing over a bridge that looked to all the world as if it might fall down. We prayed that our car would make it as it scrambled up the slope, thudding over the potholes made by countless wet winters.

We had fallen for this property from the very first viewing. But, whilst our new home had taken our breath away, it wasn't for the faint hearted. Made up of two cottages, now blended into one, it stood as high as the trees that surrounded it.

'It's not unlike an Irish tower house,' said Mum as she scurried about the garden, excited for us. She busied herself clearing the snow from a terracotta pot, dabbing at it with her hands, trying to uncover the snowdrops that were hidden beneath a carpet of icy white.

'Your plants will love it here, but don't transplant them yet, it's far too bitter. Leave them in the pots until spring.'

But, as the house stood on bedrock, Will and I wondered what we could ever get to grow.

Would even our roots be able to penetrate? And a new whippet pup raged about the place. Stripy like a tiger, the heart she possessed was no less brave. She was fearless and, like Merlin, she had the best sense of humour. The black whippet, now no longer a puppy, but a sleek-coated grown–up dog was bullied by her. I can't say it was a gradual beating down. She had shown him who was boss as soon as she could, in fact way before she was big enough. It had taken her precisely three seconds, hanging onto his ear, to drag him into submission. She had piddled her way into our lives, and had managed to ruin the one and only carpet in our new home, and on our very first night.

Sasha was quite happy; she had immediately made the master bedroom her own. Her vast assortment of clothes and teenage muddles soon threatened to spill out into the hallway - a good sign that she was settling in. It was Will that had gone back to the farm - alone - to say his final goodbyes.

Marie, Carla and Helena sent cards containing tender wishes, but Tommy was more pro-active. He messaged to say he would 'Come and check out the new place' in the spring. The cottages had been renovated to within an inch of their lives, meaning this house had no draughty windows, which was for the good. Our old curtains had been made to fit tiny panes of glass, but with no other houses nearby, that was the least of our worries. Our tall house stood stark against the backdrop of winter trees. Only the top attic bedroom and the kitchen seemed to hold onto memories of times past. The whole place had a stillness, offered solitude - and that was what we fell in love with. In many ways, it was similar to our beloved farm. But, of course, it couldn't be that wonderful place. We realised that you just can't move and replicate it. It takes years to build a home.

Our house move wasn't helped by the snow, or by the remote location. With only the rooks for company, we tried hard to settle. Our possessions all seemed at home; the furniture had wholeheartedly embraced the new location, with beds, wardrobes and sofas slotting in effortlessly. No, it was we humans who didn't fit so tidily into another family's house. We wished ourselves to be elsewhere, we wanted to go home.

The first few days found the place full, with everyone busy unpacking, but by Monday morning I was left alone within the walls of this silent house.

'I'll take Sasha to school, love,' Will shouted up the two flights of stairs. 'Your car won't make the track in this snow. You stay home, but *please*, see if BT will connect the business line.'

I lay in bed, as still as the forest outside, thinking about all the boxes yet to be unpacked, strewn about the place. We had done the removal ourselves with the help of a trusty green transit van; Nathan, our stoic apprentice; and an urgent need to make everything homely again as quickly as possible.

I heard the slam of the front door. Then came the faint laughter of Sasha and Will and the sound of the van starting as it grumbled its protest about having to start on yet another icy morning. As it pulled away, then disappeared down the track, the noise of the diesel engine faded. Silence. The whippets snuggled further under the duvet for warmth, surrounding me like two little canine hot water bottles. We had no heating, just a few logs. Last night, temperatures had plummeted to minus ten. I was too frightened to go downstairs. I was alone in a wood, next to the river that Marie had foretold, but she had said it would be all right.

The whippets and I weren't used to such solitude, such calmness. With the forge still based at our old farm, there was no familiar hammering. The buzz of life that we were used to was buzzing somewhere else.

Communications were a problem too. For some time now, BT and I had had an unhappy relationship. Nevertheless, I hunted out my mobile on that first bitter morning and rang them to find out why, for three days now, we hadn't been connected as agreed.

Whilst on hold, I managed to light the two fires in the house, do an entire wash at forty degrees, prepare an evening meal and locate the cat that the previous owners had left at the cottage. According to them, the cat lived outside.

'She'll be absolutely no trouble to you, we're grateful that she can stay. She's lived here for eleven years. She's a brave girl, but she wouldn't cope with the stress of moving,' they had said.

Absolutely no trouble? Well, we would see about that... but brave girl she was, the description was true – she could outmanoeuvre two whippets, as I found out later that morning.

So, in my search for a mobile signal, I found myself standing outside in a purple dressing gown and pink wellies, rattling a cat food tin with a fork, mobile tucked under my chin, when BT finally answered. Jostling with the cat food and keeping two whippets at bay, as they tended to bray like banshees at the sight of the cat, we all took off round the garden, including BT. I spotted the cat in the distance, slopping off onto the shed roof. So after forty-five minutes of holding, a person came on line.

'Hello.'

'Hello, madam, this is Sangit from Birmingham. How may I help you today?'

'Oh, at last!' I said. 'Well, I really hope you can help. You see we were meant to have an engineer visit three days ago to connect our phone line. It's been arranged for weeks. Then someone in your department said he would be here today. There is no sign of him, he was meant to be here at 8.30 am.'

'Oh dear, I'm terribly sorry about that, we are unusually busy because of the snow.'

'Yes, but...'

'Phone again tomorrow, please.'

'Well, now, look here, that's not good enough. We're trying to run a business and we pay more to have a business phone line.'

'Thank you, madam. I will give you my direct line number. You are phoning me again tomorrow then.'

I phoned Sangit every day. I phoned his boss, his supervisor, his wife. Possibly, sometimes I even spoke sternly to several of his aunts. Eventually, after three weeks without a phone line, I called the helpline again. This time, I demanded to speak to yet another manager.

'We sent an engineer,' he said.

'Yes, marvellous I'm sure, where is he?'

During the conversation, it became apparent that they had sent him to our old address.

'I've had this arranged for weeks, what's wrong with you BT people?'

Finally, however, the engineer did materialise. He looked extremely miserable and still didn't manage to connect us to the outside world.

I phoned another BT manager, to complain.

'And your engineer said to me that only daft people live in locations like this,' I told him. 'Then he said there was a problem at the exchange and he couldn't connect us – but he didn't try very hard, even after I'd given him three cups of tea. I've made forty phone calls to you now. I'm sorry, but you're not taking this seriously.'

'Thank you for your patience, madam. We should have you connected within two weeks now.'

The reply unleashed a state of utilities rage, a condition previously unknown to me. I surprised myself and the manager. I ranted on behalf of many householders in the UK who had been subjected to a BT connection situation. My final attack was desperate.

'You're all 'effin morons,' I said. Immediately, I was passed to the distressed customer team, a department that was even busier than the others.

Cut off for ten days in the snow with no heating and phone line, the house remained quiet – apart from the odd rant to a certain telephone company.

More alarmingly, the English breakfast tea bags, cheese and wine stocks were starting to look seriously depleted. I stared into the fridge at the mouse trap-sized lump of cheese and the pathetic quarter-bottle of a supermarket's finest budget-variety vino. My body functioned at its best on half Cathedral City, half dry white. I knew what I needed to survive a country winter. This was a Pinot Grigio emergency!

Eventually, my brother, Ellis, and his wife, Mags, came over for supper, bringing with them one of Mags's generous moussakas. Ellis stared out of the French windows, shaking his head in disbelief. He compounded the situation by asking, 'Why are you living here? It's even more isolated than the last place. At least that house had a lane and a neighbour. Don't you like people?'

'No, not much, at least not enough to live next door to them anyway,' I replied, swigging a glass of wine from the bottle they'd brought.

But his comment got us thinking. Had we had done the right thing in moving to the middle of nowhere? Nobody came to visit very often, apart from Mum and Sugar, and the writing group I belonged to, who braved the remoteness and the snow. Determined as ever, they arrived – they knew what was required. They brought with them cards, milk, smiles and hope. As we were all writing books, it meant we were in this together for the long haul. They put up with the cold, the track and the over-enthusiastic whippets, with their excessive greeting disorders.

But the hordes still didn't beat a way to our door.

'It's the track, it puts people off,' said Will.

'Or the cold – we so need heating,' said Sasha, pulling on another jumper, hat and gloves so that she could leave the safety of her now permanently attached Arctic sleeping bag for long enough to eat a meal. Having a bath was something else entirely; it filled even Will, the toughest amongst us, with dread.

We spent our evenings sitting in the kitchen by the wood burner trying to waft a tiny amount of warmth to our extremities. It was while we were sitting there late one night that we heard screams emanating from the top floor of the house. For the briefest of seconds, we stared at each other, then Will scraped back his chair and bounded up the stairs, taking three at a time. I followed – but perhaps a little less enthusiastically.

We found Sasha in her bedroom, underneath the covers with just her eyes peeping out. As we got to her side of her bed, she produced her shaking hand from underneath the duvet and pointed to the ceiling. The whippets who had been keeping her warm emerged from the bedclothes and poised themselves for attack. They sat upright, either side of Sasha, snarling like dogs of war.

Swooping continuously in a loop, from one end of the room then back, was the cause of all the teenage fear and canine fury – a tiny black bat. Now I don't know if you've ever tried to catch a bat but just as Will would position himself on a chair, ready to fling a coat over it, it was off again, gaining speed. We stood watching in the middle of the room as the poor creature became more and more panicked.

'Open the skylights and turn all the lights off, then let's leave it alone. See if it goes out on its own,' Will suggested.

We did as he asked and all traipsed back down two flights of stairs to wait it out. After half an hour, we tried again, padding silently back up the stairs, three humans and two whippets. Will creaked open the bedroom door as quietly as possible. We stepped over the threshold.

'Pop the little lamp on, Dizzy,' Will whispered.

We all stood still in the eerily silent room and gazed about us. The whippets gazed too, looking skyward. There was no sign of movement.

Then, suddenly, the bat made a reappearance, swooping just above the whippets' heads, sending them into a frenzy. Sasha let out another of her screams, this time even more terrifying than the last, which sent us all tearing back down the stairs again. This time, though, the bat followed us.

'Quick!' Will yelled. 'Open the front door, Sash. You stand by the stairs, Diz. Hold a coat, stop it going back up there.'

The bat was now in the kitchen. We worked hard to contain it, flapping our arms, holding up various items of clothing and dog blankets to stop it going back to its preferred winter location – the beams in Sasha's bedroom. The whippets, now thoroughly traumatised, leapt onto the sofa as one. In unison, they dived under a blanket and lay there together, shaking.

'We have to get it to go nearer to the front door,' I whispered.

'I need to Instagram, like now,' Sasha said.

Will, who was always good in an emergency, took off one of his many layers of clothes, reached up as the bat flew past his head and covered it with his sweatshirt. The bat and Will wrestled mid-air for a time until the human won the battle. Will held out his hands, where the tiny creature lay trembling.

'You're all right, mate,' he whispered softly. 'Off you go now.' It was a beautiful moment.

'I hope the cat doesn't get it,' said Sasha, ruining the ambience.

Will stood by the front door, then slowly opened his hands. The bat paused before taking off, swooping away into the inky black.

*

It was a few months after we'd left, before I realised that we could be all right again. The terrible upheaval was behind us and we had survived the move. The most important thing remained – Will, Sasha and I were all still together. A new buttermilk-coloured Aga hummed out a familiar background warmth. On the first spring-like day, we sat outside on the black iron bench made by Will and sipped cups of tea, warmed by sunshine. Together, we admired the crocuses and the delicate snowdrops that looked so fragile growing in the chipped Belfast sink. We listened to a woodpecker, far down in the woods below us. After the particularly wet and cold winter, the river, still high, raged through the valley, taking with it branches from fallen trees but, for us, it was the day when the sun and the light returned. At our old house, we had taken cuttings of the honeysuckle that grew where the dogs were buried. Later, our kind neighbour visited the deserted garden and gathered a few more shoots to try to cultivate them in her greenhouse, but out of the forty shoots, not one survived. Instead, I took the earth that I'd brought from our old home in tiny pots, scattering it into the soil at our new cottage.

I missed Merlin and our old home more and more, feeling like we'd truly left him and the past behind. I had wept, trying to accept that that part of life was behind us now.

Later, while moving one of the many weather-beaten stone containers brought with us from the farm, I noticed green shoots in one pot that I hadn't seen before – it was a healthy, thriving honeysuckle. The seeds that had germinated there must have been blown by the wind from the original plant. Strong and healthy, it had been busy growing, unnoticed, in this old container – the honeysuckle had survived.

That summer it climbed the copper drainpipe toward the sun, grasping on by tiny fronds that wrapped and curled back on each other. I touched its yellow petals and it released its delicate scent.

That day, I suddenly realised that I had let Merlin go. When I wasn't paying full attention, he had slipped away into the past. While I still longed for him, the feeling wasn't as strong as it once was. At first it made me feel uneasy that I'd allowed him to fade. As if I wasn't watching him properly, loving him like I should have been. When I conjured up his image now, it took effort. Even so, I sometimes still caught a glimpse of him, lying by me in the night. Or when there was a flash of light dancing off the water as I walked along the river bank.

*

Months later, I finally got around to unpacking one last thing – my treasures' box. The emptying of that box would mean that perhaps we were home. Reading my birth file felt stranger than ever. Perhaps because it was nine years to the day since I'd received that first letter from social services. It seemed such an appropriate day to look through it again.

The letter lay nestled between crisp, jade-green tissue paper along with children's first teeth; the faded leather collar of our first dog, Blue; and Merlin's red coat, still with the smell of him woven into its fibres. These were my secret special things.

Hidden beneath the papery sheets of the file were yellowing newspaper clippings; their black titles leaped out at me. One of them read, "Ex-soldier skis the country." There was a picture of my birth father, Tommy, with a trophy; photocopied pictures of my grandparents too. Tommy's wedding photo, except the bride had been chopped from the picture. He appeared to be celebrating his marriage alone. It looked like the bride had disappeared forever.

The clippings, photographs and birth file shifted me into another time.

I unfolded Merlin's coat, held it up to my face, inhaling the memory of his smell one last time, then wrapped up the gems of a past life and slipped the box back into the wardrobe.

CHAPTER 31

SIMILARITIES

Despite being busy with the move, Marie and I kept up our long Friday evening phone conversations. After a brief 'hallelujah moment' when BT had managed to get the phone line working for just twenty-four minutes, we were yet again without it. They were having more weather-related trouble, this time with wind. So, once again, I was sat at the kitchen table ready to call her from my mobile.

Apart from the similarities of appearance Marie and I shared (including the webbed toe, flat feet and having one boob bigger than the other), I'd soon come to realise, through our phone chats, that she'd also passed on some fairly quirky character traits, these included.

1) Fear of driving.
   'Of course, I would have liked to have learned to drive, Dervla,' said Marie, 'but it's not for me, it makes me anxious. And I'm not keen on motorways.'
2) Fear of motorways.
3) Love of cleaning.

'What have you been up to today, Marie?' I'd ask.

'Cleaning, again. What about you?'

'Cleaning.'

'We're quite similar, aren't we?' I'd say.

'You're so like me, Dervla, but you remind me of my dad, with your sense of humour and your storytelling,' Marie told me.

We hadn't met face to face so very often, over the nine years, so when we talked on the phone I had to imagine when she looked cross. Or I'd listen for the grin in her voice. I was getting to know my phone mother better and better.

'I think the humour and the storytelling is your fault, actually,' I told her.

'That's the Irish for you, love,' she said. It was always the fault of the Irish, according to Marie.

'Did I tell you about the time my dad came over from Ireland to stay with me?'

'No,' I said. But I knew I was in for a treat of a tale.

'He caused chaos. One night he took the mattress off the bed, he were age seventy, and used it as a slide to get down the stairs. He'd put our Helena on the back. First I knew of it was when they both slid into the front room.'

'He sounds a card.'

'God, he was that. He got sectioned. He only went out for a packet of fags and was gone three years.'

'What was wrong?' I asked.

'Manic depression. They call it something fancy nowadays. Bipolar, isn't it?'

'Yes...'

'And there was the anxiety,' Marie said.

Oh God, number four!

4) Anxiety.

'There's also my compulsions,' Marie sighed.

'Does anyone else suffer from any problems in the family?' I asked, tentatively.

'Well, you've met our Helena – we're all a bit touched… and I've had my problems,' she added, 'although I'm okay now, darlin', as long as I stay on the medication.'

'Have you got a compulsion now, do you think?'

'I have that – a compulsion to kill Vernon. I had a panic attack once and felt a desire to harm him with a carving knife.'

'When was this?'

'It were a while back. I wanted to kill someone, but Vernon were the only one in the house.'

'Shhh, don't be wicked,' I said.

'He can't hear me.'

But I could hear her as she clip-clopped across the kitchen on her, I guessed, massive heels, then kicked the door to the front room shut. There was a creak as she opened the fridge, tucking her walkabout phone under her chin.

'I'm on a diet, I've lost a stone and a half.'

'Blimey, you must look even lovelier.'

'I only eat strawberries. Been doing it a month.'

'What about your nutrition?'

'Oh, sod that. I feel fantastic,' she said.

I loved talking to her. She cheered me up every Friday evening with her stories.

'You should come and visit, Dervla. I haven't seen you in months. I miss you, love.'

'Why don't you come and visit us? You're more than welcome.'

'I would love to visit, but Vernon's not so well at the moment.'

She had only ever been to visit us the once, maybe it was the ghostly messages that had put her off, but I realised that if I wanted to see Marie it was always going to be me catching the train. It was easier that way. I could live two lives, one 'Up't North' where I morphed into a party-loving creature, and the other life down south, all quiet, where I created disgusting casseroles in Paula's orange Le Crueset and warmed my heart by the Aga.

What a privileged position – to be either free or cosy. I was beginning to wonder which life I preferred.

Chapter 32

And off I go again

Marie and I are sitting side by side in her backyard; perched on wooden chairs that are lined up outside the kitchen wall, as if we are waiting for a bus to arrive. We sip wine. The washing machine gurgles its waste down the drain next to us, wafting up a faint aroma of detergent. Children play in the field out the back; their thin voices weave towards us, then fall and die.

The background is normal, everyday, familiar, in the same way that Marie and I are now familiar to each other.

'Home tomorrow then, love?'

'Yes...'

'To your mum?'

I know what I'm meant to say.

I'm meant to say, 'But you're my mum, Marie.'

But I can't.

So instead I reply, 'Yes...'

Marie tilts her chin up slightly; her eyes are closed as she soaks in the last few rays of sunshine.

'Bet she'll be glad to see you.'

This isn't a question.

I watch her out of the corner of my eye and bite my lip; I don't want to make it obvious that I'm studying her reactions. She sniffs, opens her eyes, leans forward and reaches for the wine bottle that sits on a small wooden table in front of us and automatically tops up the glasses.

'Marie...'

I can't get the words out, so I roll a cigarette. It's pleasant sitting here with her, the first awkward meetings a distant memory. We seem to have reached a comfortable acceptance, perhaps something neither of us were expecting to achieve; any disappointment lies behind us.

I turn to face her.

'She'll be glad to see me, like you are when your children come over. I have my mum and you have your three children... we are friends though, Marie, aren't we?'

'Of course we are, you daft bugger.'

She strokes my elbow, then carries on.

'But I'm your mother too, Dervla. You look like me and I'm the one that carried you and brought you into this world. I named you.'

'Oh yes, of course. It's just that no one calls me Dervla anymore, except you and the doctor. I mean, not since I was in trouble at school have my family ever used that name.' I glance at her.

'You aren't ashamed of me are you, Dervla?'

'No... NO... don't be silly. How could I be? You're an amazing woman.' This time I mean it.

The silence is broken by the closing credits of *Coronation Street*. Vernon has it turned up so the whole street can hear. We carry on sitting.

'I love you darlin', always have.'

We clink plastic glasses and grin at each other. She slips her arm around my shoulders and squeezes me. I stare at the washing on the line as it's easier than making eye contact, and I notice for the first time how small Marie's pants are compared to Vernon's.

'Vernon's pants are enormous.'

'Shame he can't fill 'em,' she says.

We are nearly prostrate, the tears streaming down our faces.

'Buy him smaller ones then. Calvin Klein do all sizes.'

I fill the glasses this time, flicking my cigarette ash onto the warm tarmac.

'You're very glamorous, Marie.'

'People keep saying that.'

'Hmmm.'

'What time's your train tomorrow?'

'10.30, I've booked a taxi for 10.00,' I reply.

'Don't be stupid, Vernon will fetch you to the station. I'm not having you waste money on a cab.'

'I'm fine, please don't bother Vernon again,' I say.

But she's off through the back door and telling Vernon.

'Vernon, our Dervla wants a lift to the station tomorrow.'

In the morning, we stand in our normal little huddle by the newsagents' stall, Vernon, Marie, Carla and me. We've been saying goodbye for about fifteen minutes, now we all just want to get on with it. Then suddenly I'm bundled into the carriage, case hurled in behind me and Marie is passing in a sandwich and some fruit.

'I made this for you for the journey.'

'No!'

'Go on love.'

The train doors are slammed shut, so I push down the metal-framed half window and hang my head out. She plants two red kisses on my face; I inhale her perfume.

'Thanks for having me.'

She has my face in her hands and I blink back the tears.

Yes, thanks for having me, but we know I must leave again.

As the train chugs out of the platform, I watch her through the long windows framing the side of the train. We are moving slowly, but Marie is striding towards the exit in her high heels, leopard skin jacket, and black skinny jeans. I'm amazed by her resilience. From the back, she still looks like a girl, with slim, boy-like hips that would never give her away as having had five children.

She turns to wave, she uses her long painted nails to launch a thousand kisses, blowing the caresses along her hands and letting the affection float toward me. Just before she reaches the exit she stops and stares.

'Love you, Dizzy,' she calls.

At last she has called me by my proper name.

CHAPTER 33

ROOTS

What with the work happening at the cottage to make it more habitable, it has been months since I've been able to take time out to go to Sheffield.

Now I feel grubby and weary from six hours of travelling, beginning with carting my luggage across London and onto the Sheffield train. I have the laptop containing the story about finding Marie with me. Already, I feel nervous about what she will make of it. I heave the case onto the tube for a fourth time so I can make the King's Cross connection.

In Sheffield, Marie is waiting for me at the top of the escalator.

Her outstretched arms are ready to embrace me, when I see her face, full of welcome, the tiredness melts away. On this journey, I surprise myself. This time, I realise that I really am travelling with an open heart.

Vernon's silver car is parked just outside the train station in its normal preferred spot. I climb into the back seat and we head off.

As soon as we get to the bungalow, Vernon is away in the front room to watch the telly. He closes the door firmly behind him so as not to be disturbed. The smell of Domestos is as present and familiar as ever.

Within minutes, I have my arms around Marie's neck, kissing her face.

'I've missed you,' I whisper. 'I've missed out on you.'

'I'm sorry, darlin', I'm so sorry.'

'Don't be sorry.'

On the second day of my visit, I set Marie up at her tiny formica kitchen table with the laptop, gave her a quick lesson in how to use a wireless mouse, then left her there so I can nip out for a smoke. I've finished writing. Finally, she can read our story.

When I come back inside, I fret about in her kitchen, picking up the dishcloth to wipe surfaces, setting and putting away until everything is neat and orderly. I realise that we have swapped places; now it's me with the dishcloth, Marie sitting in front of the laptop. Six hours into reading, she finally lifts her head up from the screen.

'Send Vernon out for fish and peas,' she says. 'I need some dinner, then I'll read the rest.'

'Are you all right? Shall I delete the whole thing?' I ask.

'No, you won't delete it,' she says, smiling. 'But, I'm sorry, I can't do the Riverdance, Dervla.'

'It's never too late.'

'And you have made me out as being a bit plastic looking,' she continued, turning her face away.

'Oh dear, I'm so sorry, I'll change it. Or I could forget about the whole thing.'

'No, it's very important that you don't. But you haven't shown how hard it's been for me. When I lost my babies, it was the worst time of my life. No-one can know, I suppose. Unless you've lost children, you can't know.'

Right there, in that moment, I properly let Marie into my life. Which made it easier than ever before to be with her. This visit was wonderful. Marie was allowed to fuss over me, hug and kiss me. Cook me food, which was what she had longed to do all along. It was a special time for both of us. Up until then, there had always been this anxiety, this feeling of too great a difference. I no longer wanted her at arm's length.

We were just finishing off our fish and peas when Vernon got up from the sofa and walked towards the telly. He leaned over, reaching behind the screen to turn it off at the plug. Marie and I stared at each other in disbelief, waiting for Vernon's explanation – some pearls of wisdom from hitherto unsuspected depths, perhaps? This could be a life-changing moment.

'That's the first time that telly's been off in our house, Dervla, for twenty-eight years, apart from three days in 1994 when we held a wake for one of my ladies, Kathleen,' says Marie.

'That were a prolonged period of mourning,' replies Vernon. 'I missed a week of *Corrie* and I didn't even properly know Kathleen.'

'You had enough of the telly, Vernon?' I ask.

'Oh no, love, it just needs rebooting.'

Vernon fettles with the remote control, then presses it into action. A look of relief crosses his face when the screen springs back to life again. He settles back into position, leaning his head against the vast leather sofa.

'When you die, Vernon, we could just have you stuffed and leave you sitting there. Marie wouldn't even notice,' I say.

'Well, make sure you put the remote in me hand, like this.'

He holds his right arm out in front of him to mimic the position, thumb poised over the control and stares, blank faced, straight ahead of him.

'I only married him for a bet,' says Marie. 'My mate said she'd give me a tenner if I could ger 'im to take me home. I only did it for a laugh.'

'You're not laughing now are you?' I say.

'Twenty-eight years,' Vernon says, giving Marie a loving glance.

Later, I gave her my mobile phone, and she texted Tommy about the book.

'Looking forward to reading it,' he replies. 'I want you to remember, Marie, that I never stopped thinking about you. I've never stopped loving you both.'

My mum had been right – there was enough love to go around. We were a funny family alright – but maybe not so different from other people's.

*

From my windows at home, the view is of a forest – immature saplings struggling to reach the light, shaded by the more mature, taller trees. Above ground each stand alone, but my thoughts travel to underneath the soil where the roots that give the trees their vital nourishment entwine together. Below the surface, unseen, it is their conjoined root systems that sustain strength and growth, and extend amazing distances.

Through my ten years of travelling with uncertainty, shifting places and emotions, a wonderful family of strays and relations is now gathered around me. Finally, I have my roots. And I know that their strength and scope is truly astonishing.

ACKNOWLEDGEMENTS

Thank you Frances and Alison for Bootcamp, Jane and Jill for sorting out the initial muddle, Rosie Lowe and all at Matador, and all at Silver Crow.

To Malcolm, Jackie, Christine, Carla and Cazzy, thank you for keeping me going.

Joffre White, thank you for answering a lot of questions, you also make the best coffee.

Many thanks to the Wednesday Writers – Mary, Sue, Liz, Wendy, Alphonse, specifically Brenda Bannister. I'm grateful for all your help, but especially Gill Harry, for your endless support and because you understood why it was so important.

My grateful thanks, Will, for your kindness, and for sorting everything out; Sasha, for your patience and for making me laugh; and Sugar for joining me – everything is always more fun with you.

But most importantly, thank you, Mum, for not minding.